AQA GCSE Mathematics

Glyn Payne   Ron Holt   Mavis Rayment   Ian Robinson

Foundation

Practice Book

www.heinemann.co.uk
✓ Free online support
✓ Useful weblinks
✓ 24 hour online ordering

01865 888058

Heinemann

Inspiring generations

Heinemann Educational Publishers
Halley Court, Jordan Hill, Oxford OX2 8EJ
Part of Harcourt Education
© Harcourt Education Ltd 2006
Heinneman is the registered trademark of Harcourt Education Limited

First published 2006

10 09 08 07 06
10 9 8 7 6 5 4 3 2 1

British Library Cataloguing in Publication Data is available
from the British Library on request.

10-digit ISBN: 0 435533 71 1
13-digit ISBN: 978 0 435533 71 7

Edited by Sarah Findlay
Typeset by Tech-Set Ltd, Gateshead, Tyne and Wear
Original illustrations © Harcourt Education Limited, 2006
Illustrated by Adrian Barclay
Cover design by mccdesign
Printed in the United Kingdom by Scotprint
Cover photo: Alamy Images ©

Acknowledgements
Harcourt Education Ltd would like to thank those schools who helped with the development and
trialling of this course.

The author and publisher would like to thank the following individuals and organisations for
permission to reproduce photographs:
Photos.com pp **1**, **50**; Corbis pp **9**, **12**, **79**, **85**; Getty Images/PhotoDisc pp **11**, **87**;
Harcourt Education Ltd/Gareth Boden pp **41**, **64**; Alamy Images pp **44**, **69**, **102**;
Harcourt Education Ltd/Chrissie Martin pp **46**, **138**;
Harcourt Education Ltd/Tudor Photography pp **51**; Getty Images pp **67**;
Action+/Neale Haynes pp **72**; Harcourt Eductiona Ltd/Trevor Clifford pp **83**;
Richard Smith pp **96**; Rex features pp **98**

Every effort has been made to contact copyright holders of material reproduced in this book. Any
omissions will be rectified in subsequent printings if notice is given to the publishers.

Tel: 01865 888058   www.heinemann.co.uk   www.tigermaths.co.uk

Exercise 1i

Links: 1A–D

What you should know

The value of each digit in a number depends upon its position.
Read numbers from the left. The one with the largest digit in the highest place value column is the biggest.

1 Write down the value of the bold digit in these numbers.
   (a) 7**6**32
   (b) 487**5**
   (c) 1**9**521
   (d) 16**4**78
   (e) 2**6**3 100

Examples:

324 is 3 hundred, 4 tens and 2 units

12**5**736
12**6**439

126 439 is the biggest.

2 Write these numbers in words.
   (a) 324
   (b) 15 400
   (c) 28 003
   (d) 6 000 060

3 A counter in a factory showed that 1 340 073 safety pins had been made one day.

   (a) Write the number in words.

   (b) Write the value of the 4 in this number.

4 Write these numbers from smallest to largest.
   (a) 47   103   38   114   92   201   67
   (b) 18 432   17 984   18 423   17 433   18 439
   (c) 1 253 431   1 346 432   1 254 430

5 True or false?
   (a) $35 > 53$
   (b) $3424 > 899$
   (c) $5 < 4 < 11$
   (d) $852 > 794 > 749$

6 Write down a value for n in the following:
   (a) $763 < n < 765$
   (b) $12 462 > n > 12 459$

n can be any whole numbers.

Exercise 1ii

Links: 1E, 1F, 1I

What you should know

Sum, plus, find the total of, how much and altogether, all mean add.
Times and product mean multiply.

1 Work out
   (a) $468 + 72 + 9$
   (b) $1387 + 15 + 372 + 5984$

2 This table shows the number of newspapers and magazines a girl delivers each day.

Mon	Tue	Wed	Thu	Fri	Sat	Sun
84	84	59	172	131	123	132

(a) How many are delivered on a weekend?

(b) What is the total for the whole week?

3 Find the sum of 1373, 39 and 483.

4 Copy and complete this multiplication square.

×	7	16	312
4			
8			
9			

5 A bus holds 42 people. Boxton Motors have 15 buses. How many people can they transport?

6 Find the product of 586 and 34.

UAM **7** How many packets will I have altogether if I have 15 boxes containing 24 packets each and 18 boxes containing 36 packets each?

UAM **8** 6 friends want to go on holiday. It costs £247 each. There is a fuel surcharge of £37 per person and the taxi to the airport costs a total of £24. What is the total cost of the holiday for the 6 friends?

Exercise 1iii

Links: 1G–I

What you should know

Minus, difference, take away and how much more than, all mean subtract.

Share, how many ... are there in ..., and how many times does ... go into ..., all mean divide.

1. Work out

(a) 392 − 247   (b) 623 − 482   (c) 200 − 37

(d) 350 − 243   (e) 4060 − 157   (f) 8000 − 672

2. A school is trying to raise £1000 for a charity. They have £752 so far. How much more do they need?

3. John travels 1032 miles to work in a year. Sally travels 846 miles. What is the difference in their milage?

4 Work out
   (a) $56 \div 7$ (b) $738 \div 6$ (c) $816 \div 8$
   (d) $775 \div 25$ (e) $651 \div 31$ (f) $609 \div 29$

5 A school shares 256 exercise books between 8 classes.
   How many books does each class get?

6 4 friends share 300 hazel nuts between them.
   (a) How many does each receive?

   Mark joins them and they decide to give him 18 nuts each.
   (b) How many nuts will the 4 friends have each now?
   (c) How many more nuts does Mark have than his 4 friends?

7 There are 322 bulbs to be planted in 23 flower beds.
   If they are shared equally, how many bulbs will be planted in each bed?

Exercise 1iv

Links: 1J

> ### What you should know
>
> The order of operations is:
>
> Brackets ⟶ Indices ⟶ Divide / Multiply ⟶ Add / Subtract

1 Work out
   (a) $6 + 5 \times 4$ (b) $16 - 3 \times 4 + 5$ (c) $2 \times 3 + 3 \times 5$

2 Work out
   (a) $3 \times (4 + 3)$ (b) $8 + (19 - 4) \div 5$ (c) $3(28 - 3)$

> $3(28 - 3)$ is another way of writing $3 \times (28 - 3)$.

3 Find the value of
   (a) $2^2 \times 3^2$ (b) $4 + 5 \times 6^2$
   (c) $7 \times (4 + 2^2) + 5$ (d) $5^2(8 - 3)$

4 Copy these statements and put in the correct signs to make them true.
   You may need to add brackets.
   (a) $5\ [\ ]\ 4\ [\ ]\ 3 = 23$
   (b) $7\ [\ ]\ 9\ [\ ]\ 2 = 32$
   (c) $4\ [\ ]\ 5\ [\ ]\ 6\ [\ ]\ 3 = 38$
   (d) $3\ [\ ]\ 2^2\ [\ ]\ 5\ [\ ]\ 6 = 29$

5 Simon and Alice were doing this calculation.

$$\frac{4 + (10^2 - 8^2)}{2 \times 6 - 2^2}$$

Simon got an answer of 10, Alice got 5. Who is right?
Show your working to explain your answer.

Exercise 1v

Links: 1K, 1L, 1N

What you should know

Numbers can be positive or negative. You can use rules of sign for adding and subtracting positive and negative numbers.

> $+ +$ is the same as $+$
> $- -$ is the same as $+$
> $- +$ is the same as $-$
> $+ -$ is the same as $-$

1 What will the following temperatures be in degrees Celcius after
   (i) a rise of 7°   **(ii)** a fall of 9°?
   (a) 2°C   **(b)** −5°C   **(c)** −13°C   **(d)** 8°C

> A number without a sign in front is always positive.

2 The temperature at different hights on a mountain were
   −2°C   −9°C   −25°C   −14°C   −12°C
   Place these in order from warmest to coldest.

3 Work out
   (a) −2 + (+5)   **(b)** 8 + (−3)   **(c)** 5 + (+5)
   (d) −3 + (−8)   **(e)** −3 + 3   **(f)** −2 + (−6)

4 Complete these subtractions
   (a) +4 − (+9)   **(b)** −1 − (+4)   **(c)** 6 − (−12)

5 Write in the missing number to make these statements true.
   (a) +5 + [ ] = 3   **(b)** −6 + [ ] = 3
   (c) −4 − [ ] = −11   **(d)** −6 − [ ] = 8

6 **(a)** What is the difference between −15°C and −23°C?
   (b) In London the temperature is 12°C. In Madrid it is 17°C higher.
   What is the temperature in Madrid?

Exercise 1vi

Links: 1M, 1N

What you should know

You can use rules of sign for multiplying and dividing positive and negative numbers.

> $+ \times + = +$ $+ \times - = -$
> $- \times - = +$ $- \times + = -$
>
> $+ \div + = +$ $+ \div - = -$
> $- \div - = +$ $- \div + = -$

1 Work out

    (a) $(+7) \times (-5)$ **(b)** $(-3) \times (+9)$ **(c)** $4 \times (-6)$

    (d) $(-9) \times (-8)$ **(e)** $(+3) \times (+7)$ **(f)** $4 \times (-2) \times (-3)$

> "Like signs make a positive. Different signs make a negative."

2 Complete these divisions.

    (a) $(-25) \div (-5)$ **(b)** $(-24) \div (+8)$ **(c)** $35 \div (-7)$

    (d) $+77 \div -11$ **(e)** $-42 \div 6$ **(f)** $-18 \div -9$

3 Copy and complete the following by putting in the missing number.

    (a) $(-8) \times [\ ] = -24$ **(b)** $(-50) \div [\ ] = +2$

    (c) $21 \div [\ \ ] = -3$ **(d)** $(-4) \times [\ ] \times (-5) = -60$

4 Copy the box and shade in the correct answers.

-15	-8	$+18$	$+5$	$+3$	-2	-7	$+8$	-5	-4
$+6$	$+30$	$+2$	-1	-17	$+16$	-6	-9	$+36$	-16
-54	-14	-40	$+19$	-18	-3	$-45.$	$+1$	$+12$	-12

$(-4) + (-2)$	$(-9) - (-5)$	$7 \times (-2)$	$(+3) \times (-5)$
$(-6) \times (-2)$	$(-12) \div (-4)$	$9 \div (-3)$	$16 - (-2)$
$(-8) + (-9)$	$(+5) \times (+6)$	$(-24) - (-6)$	$64 \div (-8)$
$(+12) + (-17)$	$(-42) \div (+6)$	$(-8) - 8$	$9 \times (-5)$
$13 + (-15)$	$(-6) \times (-6)$		

Exercise 1vii

Links: 1O, 1Q

> ## What you should know
>
> The value of each number in a decimal number depends on its position.
>
> To order decimal numbers, read from the left. The number with the highest digit in the highest place value column is the biggest.

1 Write the value of the 3 in each of these numbers.

    (a) 0.03 **(b)** 0.3 **(c)** 0.003

2 Write the following as decimal numbers.

    (a) $\dfrac{7}{10}$ **(b)** $\dfrac{4}{100}$ **(c)** $\dfrac{2}{10} + \dfrac{3}{100} + \dfrac{2}{1000}$

> *Example:*
>
> $0.624 = 6$ tenths, $\left(\dfrac{6}{10}\right)$
>
> $+$
>
> 2 hundredths $\left(\dfrac{2}{100}\right)$
>
> $+$
>
> 4 thousandths $\left(\dfrac{4}{1000}\right)$

3 Which number in each pair is the smaller?

    (a) 0.08 and 0.008   **(b)** 1.25 and 1.2

    (c) 3.823 and 3.831   **(d)** 4.61 and 4.59

> *Example:*
>
> 1.235
> 1.225   1.2 is the same.
>   ↑   3 is bigger than 2 in
>   this column, so
>   1.235 is the
>   biggest.

4 Write these numbers in order from smallest to largest.

    (a) 1.3   1.32   1.4   1.31

    (b) 4.32   4.35   4.326   4.33

    (c) 12.842   12.84   12.804   12.844

5 Write down a value of n in the following:

    (a) $7.3 > n > 7.5$ **(b)** $6.43 > n > 6.44$

> n can be any number.

6 Place the heights of these four friends in order, tallest first.

    1.345 m   1.354 m   1.428 m   1.35 m

Exercise 1viii

Links: 1P

> ## What you should know
>
> To multiply and divide by 10, 100 and 1000, move digits to the left to multiply and move the digits to the right to divide. Remember to add place holders when needed.
>
> ×/÷ by 10: move 1 place.
> ×/÷ by 100: move 2 places.
> ×/÷ by 1000: move 3 places.

1 Work out the following:

    (a) 3.62×10 **(b)** 4.95×100 **(c)** 1.165×1000

    (d) 4.2×100 **(e)** 6.325×100 **(f)** 4.3×1000

> A place value table can help.

2 Work out the following:

    (a) $8.3 \div 10$ **(b)** $12.32 \div 100$ **(c)** $1325 \div 1000$

    (d) $9 \div 10$ **(e)** $0.3 \div 100$ **(f)** $15.2 \div 1000$

3 What would be the cost of 100 books priced at £1.23 each?

4 The mass of 100 boxes of chocolates is 56.5 kg. What is the mass of one box?

5 A meal costs £4.25. What will 10 similar meals cost?

6 The capacity of a can of lemonade is 330 m*l*. What will be the total volume of 200 cans in litres?

7 A coil of wire is 5.5 m long. It is to be cut into 100 equal pieces. How long will each piece be in centimetres?

8 What is $2.76 \times 10 \div 100 \div 10 \times 100$?

Exercise 1ix

Links: 1R, 1S, 1V

> ## What you should know
>
> To add and subtract decimals, line up the decimal points underneath each other.

1. Add each of the following:
   (a) $0.6 + 12.4 + 1.59 + 0.89$
   (b) $0.235 + 6 + 1.5$

2. Work out
   (a) $3.8 - 2.9$ (b) $6.27 - 3.45$
   (c) $7.5 - 2.13$ (d) $8 - 2.47$

3. Amy is 1.45 m tall and Ranjit is 1.53 m tall.
   How much taller is Ranjit than Amy?

4. On a night out, Molly spent £1.45 on bus fares, £3.25 on a cinema ticket, 84p on a drink and £1.40 on a hotdog.
   (a) How much did she spend?
   (b) How much change will she have from £10?

5. Paul needs a total of 2.375 m of pipe to complete a job. He has a piece 1.4 m long, another piece 0.85 m long and a third piece 0.345 m long. How much pipe will he have left over?

6. Tom and Gary have four attempts at completing a puzzle in the quickest time. Here are their results (in seconds).

Tom	48.73	46.8	53.25	44.05
Gary	55.32	47.5	43.75	42.79

   (a) What is the difference in the total time for each boy?
   (b) What was the difference between the fastest and slowest individual times?

⊞ Exercise 1x

Links: 1T, 1U

> ### What you should know
>
> When multiplying decimals, count the total number of decimal places in the numbers in the question. The answer must have this number of decimal places.
>
> When dividing decimals, multiply both numbers by 10, 100 or 1000 to make the number you are dividing by a whole number.

1 Find the value of

    (a) 47×0.4 **(b)** 0.25×7 **(c)** 122×0.36

    (d) 2.8×1.3 **(e)** 0.29×0.21 **(f)** 24.7×3.2

> *Examples:*
> $$1.\underline{3} \times 0.\underline{2} = 0.2\underline{6}$$
> $$\frac{12.24}{0.3} \; \frac{\times 10}{\times 10} = \frac{122.4}{3}$$

2 A rectangle is 8.5 cm long by 7.5 cm wide. What is the area of the rectangle?

> Area = length × width.

3 Prawns costs £4.06 per kilogramme. How much will 3.5 kg cost?

4 Work out

    (a) $13.76 \div 4$ **(b)** $27.2 \div 5$ **(c)** $1.938 \div 6$

    (d) $6.4 \div 0.4$ **(e)** $1.5 \div 0.03$ **(f)** $14.4 \div 1.2$

5 The cost of five t-shirts was £11.75. What was the cost of one t-shirt?

6 The area of a rectangular lawn is 51.46 m². If the length is 8.3 m, what is the width?

> Width = area ÷ length.

7 Jason earns £6.05 per hour. He works 14 hours in a week and had £17.32 deducted for tax and national insurance. How much money did he take home?

8 A bill for books was £27.44. If each book cost 98p, how many books did I buy?

⊞ Mixed Exercise

1 **(a)** Place the following numbers in order, from smallest to largest.

        23 486   23 475   23 485   23 491

    (b) What is the value of the digit 2 in these numbers?

    (c) Write the first number in words.

2 There are 13 boxes containing 27 jigsaws. How many jigsaws are there altogether?

3 Jane earns £12050 and Kim earns £11 666. What is the difference in their earnings?

4 Work out

(a) $9^2 + 7 \times 8$ (b) $(4 + 6) \times (24 - 18)$

5 Lobster costs £11.10 per kilogramme. What will a 0.7 kg lobster cost?

6 Give a value for n (any number) in the following expressions:

(a) $137 < n < 139$ (b) $2.4 > n > 2.3$

7 Find the total of 79, 138, 6 and 123.

8 The total cost of an outing for 36 people was £252. How much did it cost for one person?

9 A DVD player has a mass of 2.31 kg. What would 10 weigh?

10 A piece of wood is 9.4 m long. Another piece is 7.36 m long. What is the difference in length of the two pieces of wood?

11 Wire that is 47.2 m long is cut into pieces 0.4 m long. How many pieces will I have?

12 If 100 containers have a volume of 5370 cm^3, what is the volume of one container?

Checklist

You should know about...	Grade	For more help, look back at Student Book pages...
place value	G/F	1–5, 27–28
ordering numbers	G/F	6–9, 31–33
solving problems with numbers	G/F	9–17
order of operations	G/F	17–19
solving problems with positive and negative numbers	F/E	19–26
multiplying and dividing by 10, 100 and 1000	G/F	29–31
solving problems involving decimals.	G to C	34–44

2 Approximations and estimations

Exercise 2i

Links: 2A, 2B

What you should know

When rounding a number to the nearest 10, 100 or 1000, if it is halfway between two limits, round up.

When a problem does not give a whole number answer, you have to decide whether to round up or down.

1 Round to the nearest 10:

(a) 253   (b) 468   (c) 24 315

2 Round to the nearest 100:

(a) 941   (b) 32 450   (c) 1973

3 Round to the nearest 1000:

(a) 6492   (b) 84 513   (c) 9999

Example:
Nearest 10
8715 = 8720
Nearest 100
8715 = 8700
Nearest 1000
8715 = 9000

4 The number of people who applied to go on a TV quiz show was 17 385. Write this number to the nearest

(a) ten   (b) hundred   (c) thousand.

5 There are 15 chocolates in a packet. If I have 87 chocolates, how many packets can I make?

6 There are 462 supporters going to an away match. If a bus can take 41 supporters, how many buses will they need?

7 A garden has two lawns that are each 6 m long by 5 m wide and one lawn that is 12 m by 8 m. 1 kg of lawn feed covers 25 m² and one box of feed holds 2 kg. How many boxes of feed will be needed to cover the garden?

Find the area of each lawn first, using this formula:
area = length × width.

Exercise 2ii

Links: 2C

What you should know

To round to a given number of decimal places, count the number of decimal places (d.p.) you want. If the next digit is 5 or more, round up. If the next digit is 4 or less, leave it as it is.

1. Round to 1 decimal place:

(a) 9.26   (b) 7.74   (c) 4.35

Examples:
4.59 = 4.6 (to 1 d.p.)
6.532 = 6.53 (to 2 d.p.)

2 Round to 2 decimal places:

(a) 4.125   (b) 16.834   (c) 1.136

3 A dolphin measured 2.253 m. What is this to

(a) the nearest metre   (b) 1 d.p.   (c) 2 d.p.?

4 The results for a sprint are given in the table.

Position	1	2	3	4	5
Time (s)	13.245	13.262	13.289	13.753	13.985

Round each time to

(a) 2 d.p.   (b) 1 d.p.   (c) the nearest whole number.

5 Work out the following calculations and give your answer to 2 d.p.

(a) 6.25 × 4.83   (b) 0.29 ÷ 0.623   (c) 3.45 × 8.137

6 Three friends had a lottery win of £1217. If they shared it equally, how much would each receive? Give your answer to 2 d.p. Is your answer to the nearest penny, 10p or pound?

Exercise 2iii

Links: 2D

> ### What you should know
>
> To round to a given number of significant figures, start counting from the most significant figure (s.f.). Look at the next digit. If it is 5 or more, you round up the previous digit. If it is 4 or less, you leave the previous digit as it is. Use zero place holders to indicate place value.

1 Round these numbers to 1 s.f.

(a) 429   (b) 7634   (c) 18453   (d) 246875

2 Round these numbers to 1 s.f.

(a) 0.38   (b) 0.042   (c) 0.000492   (d) 0.0035

> *Examples:*
> 182.45 = 200 (to 1 s.f.)
> 0.006 27 = 0.006 (to 1 s.f.)

3 Round 8.093 correct to

(a) 1 s.f.   (b) 2 s.f.   (c) 3 s.f.

4 The lengths jumped in a competition were

5.423 m   7.045 m   6.869 m   7.072 m

Round these lengths to (a) 2 s.f.   (b) 3 s.f.

5 Work out $\dfrac{6859 \times 3504}{422}$. Give your answer to 2 s.f.

6 120 is written to 2 s.f. List all the values it could be.

Exercise 2iv

Links: 2E

What you should know

To estimate using approximations, round all of the numbers in the calculation to one s.f. then work out the answer using these rounded numbers.

1 Use approximation to estimate the answers to these calculations.

(a) 2.3×4.8

(b) 18×34

(c) $128 \div 53$

(d) $2692 \div 627$

(e) $6.25 + 8.73 - 4.6$

(f) 0.0045×0.99

Example:
$6.5 \times 4.3 \times 2.9 \approx 7 \times 4 \times 3$
≈ 84

Show all your working.

2 There are 28 tiles in a box and 54 boxes in a carton. Estimate how many tiles are there in a carton.

3 1 g of sand contains 162 grains. Estimate how many grains will be in 250 g of sand.

4 Estimate the length of 124 pieces of wire that are each 0.35 m.

5 If a DVD costs £8.99, estimate the cost of 475 DVDs.

6 A ship can travel 23.6 miles in 58 mins. Estimate how far it could travel in a day.

Mixed exercise

1 Is it true that 390 is 384 rounded to the nearest 10?

2 Round 1.263 to (a) 1 d.p. (b) 2 d.p.

3 Write these numbers to 2 s.f. (a) 347 000 (b) 0.060 25

 4 Jason travels 4.35 km each day. Estimate how far he travels in a year.

5 A table can seat 12 people. If 270 people need seating, how many tables will I need?

Checklist

You should know how to...	Grade	For more help, look back at Student Book pages...
round to 10, 100, 1000	F/G	50–54
round to decimal places	F	54–55
round to significant figures	E	56–58
estimate using approximations.	C	58–60

Exercise 3i

Links: 3A, 3B

> **What you should know**
>
> A fraction has a numerator (top number) and a denominator (bottom number).
>
> Equivalent fractions are fractions with the same value. You can find them by multiplying or dividing the numerator and denominator by the same number.

1 For each diagram write

    (i) the shaded fraction   **(ii)** the unshaded fraction.

    (a)   **(b)**   **(c)**   **(d)**

2 There are two black discs, four red discs and five green discs. What fraction of the discs are

> Find the total number of discs first.

    (a) red   **(b)** green   **(c)** not black?

3 Which of these fractions are equivalent to $\frac{3}{4}$?

$$\frac{6}{8} \quad \frac{8}{12} \quad \frac{15}{20} \quad \frac{25}{30} \quad \frac{12}{16} \quad \frac{18}{25}$$

> *Example:*
>
> $$\overset{\div 2}{\frown} \quad \overset{\times 5}{\frown}$$
> $$\frac{2}{5} = \frac{4}{10} = \frac{20}{50}$$

4 Copy and complete these equivalent fractions.

    (a) $\dfrac{2}{5} = \dfrac{\square}{10} = \dfrac{6}{\square} = \dfrac{20}{\square} = \dfrac{\square}{45}$

    (b) $\dfrac{\square}{6} = \dfrac{10}{12} = \dfrac{\square}{66} = \dfrac{15}{\square} = \dfrac{60}{\square}$

5 Sarah's test results were $\frac{16}{20}$ for history and $\frac{48}{80}$ for science. Write these fractions in their simplest form.

> The simplest form is when there is no number that will divide into the numerator and denominator.

Exercise 3ii

Links: 3C, 3E, 3F

> **What you should know**
>
> To put fractions in order, they need to have the same denominator.
>
> To write an improper fraction as mixed numbers, divide the numerator by the denominator and write down the whole numbers part. The remainder gives you the fractional part.
>
> To write a mixed number as an improper fraction, multiply the whole number part by the denominator of the fractional part. Add the fractional part of your answer to your first result.

1 Change these fractions to equivalent fractions, then write them using $<$ or $>$.

(a) $\frac{2}{5}$ $\frac{3}{10}$ (b) $\frac{7}{8}$ $\frac{3}{4}$ (c) $\frac{5}{6}$ $\frac{3}{5}$ (d) $\frac{2}{3}$ $\frac{3}{4}$

2 Write these improper fractions as mixed numbers.

(a) $\frac{7}{2}$ (b) $\frac{18}{5}$ (c) $\frac{24}{7}$ (d) $\frac{48}{11}$

3 Write these mixed numbers as improper fractions.

(a) $2\frac{1}{3}$ (b) $3\frac{5}{6}$ (c) $1\frac{5}{9}$ (d) $10\frac{3}{8}$

4 Copy and complete with the correct sign $<$, $>$ or $=$.

(a) $2\frac{2}{5}$ ☐ $\frac{11}{5}$ (b) $\frac{17}{4}$ ☐ $4\frac{1}{4}$ (c) $3\frac{5}{9}$ ☐ $\frac{34}{9}$

5 Paul had $1\frac{3}{4}$ bars of chocolate. Ann had $\frac{17}{10}$ bars and Molly had $\frac{7}{5}$ bars.

(a) Who had the most chocolate?

(b) Who had the least chocolate?

Example:

$\frac{3}{5}$ $\frac{4}{10}$ $\frac{12}{15}$

$\frac{3}{5}$ $\frac{4}{10} = \frac{2}{5}$ $\frac{12}{15} = \frac{4}{5}$

In order: $\frac{4}{10}$ $\frac{3}{5}$ $\frac{12}{15}$

$>$ means more than.
$<$ means less than.

Example:

$\frac{12}{5} = \frac{5}{5} + \frac{5}{5} + \frac{2}{5} = 2\frac{2}{5}$

Example:

$2\frac{1}{3} = \frac{3}{3} + \frac{3}{3} + \frac{1}{3} = \frac{7}{3}$

Change the mixed numbers into improper fractions first and then into fractions with the same denominator.

Exercise 3iii

Links: 3D

What you should know

To find a fraction of a quantity, remember that 'of' means multiply.

1 Work out

(a) $\frac{1}{3}$ of $12l$ (b) $\frac{1}{7}$ of $84\,\text{cm}$

(c) $\frac{3}{4}$ of £36   (d) $\frac{4}{9}$ of $45\,\text{kg}$.

2 Which is bigger?

(a) $\frac{2}{5}$ of 40 or $\frac{2}{3}$ of 33   (b) $\frac{5}{6}$ of 54 or $\frac{7}{10}$ of 70

Example:

To find $\frac{3}{5}$ of 10, you can:

find $\frac{1}{5}$ of 10 $= \frac{10}{5} = 2$

Then

$\frac{3}{5} = 3 \times (\frac{1}{5}$ of 10$) = 3 \times 2 = 6$.

3 John's garden covers $144\,\text{m}^2$. $\frac{3}{8}$ of his garden is lawn and $\frac{1}{6}$ is a vegetable patch.

(a) What is the area of the lawn?

(b) What is the area of the vegetable patch?

(c) How much of the garden is neither lawn nor vegetable patch?

4 Sally gets £86 for her birthday. She spends $\frac{7}{12}$ on a pair of trousers and $\frac{3}{8}$ on a DVD.

(a) How much did her trousers cost? Give your answer to the nearest penny.

(b) How much money does she have left?

Find your full answer before you round it to the nearest penny.

Exercise 3iv

What you should know

You can only add and subtract fractions if they have the same denominator. You change them into equivalent fractions to do this.

1 Work out

(a) $\frac{4}{11} + \frac{5}{11}$

(b) $\frac{2}{5} + \frac{1}{2}$

(c) $\frac{7}{10} + \frac{4}{5} + \frac{3}{4}$

Example:

$\frac{1}{2} + \frac{2}{3}$

$\frac{1}{2} = \frac{3}{6}$ $\frac{2}{3} = \frac{4}{6}$

$\frac{1}{2} + \frac{2}{3} = \frac{3}{6} + \frac{4}{6} = \frac{7}{6}$ or $1\frac{1}{6}$

2 Copy and complete the following, giving your answers as mixed numbers.

(a) $1\frac{1}{2} + 1\frac{3}{10}$

(b) $3\frac{1}{3} + 1\frac{3}{5}$

(c) $2\frac{1}{4} + 2\frac{5}{6} + 1\frac{2}{3}$

3 If I add $12\frac{1}{2}$ m of line to the $6\frac{3}{4}$ m of line on my fishing rod, how much line will I have altogether?

4 Work out

(a) $\frac{5}{9} - \frac{2}{9}$

(b) $\frac{5}{8} - \frac{1}{4}$

(c) $\frac{3}{5} - \frac{1}{10}$

5 Copy and complete the following:

(a) $2\frac{2}{5} - 1\frac{3}{4} =$

(b) $3\frac{3}{8} - 1\frac{5}{6} =$

(c) $2\frac{1}{3} - 1\frac{3}{4} =$

You can change the mixed numbers into improper fractions first.

6 On a trip, we had $2\frac{1}{2}l$ of water. We brought $1\frac{3}{4}l$ home. How much water did we drink?

7 I used $1\frac{3}{8}$ kg of flour from a bag holding $2\frac{1}{2}$ kg. How much flour is left in the bag?

8 I have two pieces of wire that are $3\frac{3}{8}$ m and $2\frac{2}{5}$ m long. I use $4\frac{7}{10}$ m. How much wire do I have left?

Exercise 3v

What you should know

To multiply fractions, you multiply the numerators and then multiply the denominators.
To divide fractions, you invert the fraction you are dividing by and change the sign to multiply.

1 Work out

(a) $\frac{2}{5} \times \frac{3}{7}$

(b) $\frac{1}{3} \times \frac{5}{8}$

(c) $\frac{3}{4} \times \frac{4}{7}$

(d) $\frac{5}{8}$ of $\frac{4}{15}$

(e) $\frac{2}{3}$ of $\frac{9}{14}$

(d) $\frac{1}{2} \times \frac{3}{4} \times \frac{8}{9}$.

Example:

$\frac{1}{2} \times \frac{3}{5} = \frac{3}{10}$

2 Work out

(a) $1\frac{2}{3} \times 1\frac{4}{5}$ (b) $2\frac{1}{2} \times 1\frac{2}{5}$ (c) $1\frac{3}{4} \times 2\frac{2}{3} \times 1\frac{2}{7}$

3 What is the area of a rectangle that is $3\frac{3}{8}$ inches long by $1\frac{7}{9}$ inches wide?

4 Work out

(a) $\frac{2}{3} \div \frac{3}{4}$ (b) $\frac{2}{5} \div \frac{7}{10}$ (c) $\frac{1}{4} \div \frac{5}{8}$

(d) $9 \div \frac{3}{5}$ (e) $\frac{4}{7} \div 8$ (f) $\frac{5}{9} \div \frac{5}{6}$

> **Example:**
>
> $\frac{1}{3} \div \frac{1}{2} = \frac{1}{3} \times \frac{2}{1} = \frac{2}{3}$
>
> Change mixed numbers into improper fractions.

5 Copy and complete the following divisions.

(a) $2\frac{1}{4} \div 1\frac{1}{2} =$ (b) $2\frac{7}{10} \div 1\frac{4}{5} =$ (c) $3\frac{1}{3} \div 2\frac{6}{7} =$

6 How many pieces of wire $\frac{3}{8}$ m long can I cut from a piece $3\frac{3}{4}$ m long?

7 To find how many kilograms of feed you need for a lawn, you find the area and then divide by $3\frac{3}{5}$. If my lawn is $12\frac{1}{2}$ m by $7\frac{1}{5}$ m, how much feed will I need?

> Area = length × width.

Exercise 3vi

Links: 3K, 3L

What you should know

To change a percentage into a fraction or a decimal, divide by 100.

To change a decimal or fraction into a percentage, multiply by 100 (you can change the fraction into a decimal first).

1 Write these percentages as fractions, and give your answer in its simplest form.

(a) 23%   (b) 40%   (c) 72%   (d) $12\frac{1}{2}\%$ (e) 5%

> **Example:**
>
> $13\% = \frac{13}{100}$ or 0.13

2 Write the percentages above as decimals.

3 Dave's test results were 72% for history and $\frac{17}{25}$ for geography. By changing both scores into fractions, find out which was the highest score.

> **Example:**
>
> $\frac{2}{5} = 0.4 \times 100\% = 40\%$

4 Write the following numbers as percentages and then put them in order, from smallest to largest.

     0.58 $\frac{5}{8}$ $\frac{17}{40}$ 0.583

5 Copy and complete the following table of equivalent fractions, decimals and percentages.

Fraction	Percentage	Decimal
$\frac{2}{5}$		
		0.45
	$12\frac{1}{2}\%$	

> Write the fractions in their simplest form.

Exercise 3vii

Links: 3M, 3N

> ## What you should know
>
> To change a fraction into a decimal, divide the numerator by the denominator.
>
> To write a recurring decimal, use *dot* notation over the recurring pattern.
>
> To write a truncating decimal or recurring decimal as a fraction, place the number over 10, 100 or 1000 (the smallest place value). For recurring decimals, eliminate the recurring part by multiplying and then subtracting.

1 Change these fractions into decimals. Write the full calculator display, and indicate whether the decimal is truncating, recurring or non-recurring.

Example:
$\frac{3}{5} = 3 \div 5 = 0.6$

   (a) $\frac{4}{5}$ **(b)** $\frac{7}{8}$ **(c)** $\frac{5}{9}$ **(d)** $\frac{1}{6}$ **(e)** $\frac{23}{7}$

2 Change these fractions into decimals. Write
  (i) the full calculator display, and
  (ii) the recurring decimal, using the dot notation.

Example:
$0.454545... = 0.4\dot{5}$

   (a) $\frac{7}{11}$ **(b)** $\frac{7}{9}$ **(c)** $\frac{5}{6}$ **(d)** $\frac{7}{12}$ **(e)** $\frac{3}{7}$

3 Write these decimals as fractions.

Example:
$0.125 = \frac{125}{1000} = \frac{1}{8}$

   (a) 0.7   **(b)** 0.24   **(c)** 0.375

4 Copy and complete these calculations, converting the recurring decimals into fractions.

   (a) $x = 0.22222....$
      $10x = \square$
       $9x = 2$
     so fraction $= \frac{2}{9}$

   (b) $x = 0.242424....$
     $\square x = 24.2424....$
     $99x = \square$
     so fraction $= \frac{24}{99}$

Give your answer in its simplest form.

Mixed Exercise

1 Tom collects model cars. He has seven saloons, eleven hatchbacks and six sports cars. What fraction of his cars are

   (a) saloons   **(b)** sports cars   **(c)** not saloons?

2 Put these fractions in order, smallest first.
    $\frac{3}{8}$ $\frac{1}{4}$ $\frac{5}{16}$

3 Mark has to pay $\frac{2}{15}$ of his earnings in tax. He earns £264 per week.

   (a) How much tax will he pay?

   (b) How much money will he take home?

4 I had $3\frac{1}{2}$ bars of chocolate. I ate $1\frac{1}{4}$ bars and Alan ate $\frac{7}{10}$ of a bar. How much chocolate is left?

5 It takes $2\frac{1}{2}$ kg of potatoes to fill a tub. How many kilograms of potatoes will I need to fill $3\frac{1}{4}$ tubs?

6 Write the following numbers in order, with the smallest first.

23% $\frac{3}{20}$ 0.22 $\frac{7}{25}$ 22.7% $\frac{1}{5}$

7 Write these numbers as fractions.

    (a) 0.36   **(b)** 0.125   **(c)** 0.777....

Checklist

You should know about...	Grade	For more help, look back at Student Book pages...
equivalent, proper and improper fractions	G/F	64−71, 73−75
fractions of a quantity	D/E	71−73
four rules for fractions	E to C	75−81
changing between percentages, fractions and decimals	G to D	82−86
writing decimals as fractions and vice versa.	G to C	86−89

Exercise 4i

Links: 4A

What you should know

You can use letters to write simple expressions.

$$3 \times x = 3x \qquad y \times y = y^2 \qquad m \times n = mn \qquad a \div 5 = \frac{a}{5}$$

1 Use algebra to write expressions for these.

(a) 3 more than x (b) 6 less than p (c) k add 1

(d) t subtract 5   (e) a take away 7   (f) f added to h

2 Write an algebraic expression for each of these.

(a) 5 times x (b) a divided by 4   (c) t multiplied by 7

(d) p lots of q (e) 10 divided by h (f) d multiplied by d

> Remember to write the number first.
>
> **Example:**
>
> $3x$ not $x3$

3 Use algebra to write expressions for these. Use x to stand for the number I choose.

(a) I choose a number and add 8.

(b) I choose a number and divide it by 3.

(c) I choose a number and multiply it by 9.

(d) I choose a number and take 4 away.

(e) I choose a number, multiply it by 4 and then add 6.

(f) I choose a number, divide it by 5 and then subtract 1.

4 Write an expression for the total cost in pounds of

(a) 5 CDs at p pounds each   (b) x DVDs at £15 each

(c) 3 CDs at c pounds each and 6 DVDs at d pounds each.

Exercise 4ii

Links: 4B

What you should know

To add and subtract terms in algebra, use the same rules as you do when working with numbers.

1 Write each of these expressions in a shorter form.

(a) $g + g + g + g$ (b) $b + b + b + b + b + b$

(c) $e + e + e$ (d) $s + s + s + s + s$

(e) $4t + 2t$ (f) $5r + r + 3r$

(g) $7i + i + 2i + i$ (h) $4p + 5p + 8p + 6p$

> Remember that y means $1y$.

2 Simplify these algebraic expressions.

(a) $8d - 3d$ (b) $4e - e$

(c) $13n - 7n$ (d) $3i + 4i - 5i$

(e) $6s + 5s - 4s$ (f) $5l - 2l + 4l$

(g) $9a - a - 4a$ (h) $8w - 6w + 7w$

(i) $3x - 5x + 7x - x$ (j) $4y - 7y + 4y$

> You can add and subtract the terms in any order you like as long as each term keeps its own sign.

3 Copy and complete each of these magic squares.

(a)

$9x$	$2x$	$7x$
$4x$		

(b)

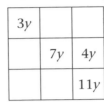

$3y$		
	$7y$	$4y$
		$11y$

> In a magic square, the sum of the expressions in each row, column and each of the two diagonals is the same.

Exercise 4iii

Links: 4C

What you should know

Terms which use the same letter are called like terms.

You can simplify algebraic expressions by collecting like terms together.

1 Simplify these expressions by collecting like terms.

(a) $3c + 5d + 4c$ (b) $2a + 4b + 5a$

(c) $7m + 3n + m$ (d) $8x + 6 + 2x + 3$

(e) $5p + q + 2p + 3q$ (f) $4f + 5g + 2f - 3g$

(g) $6z + 7 - 5z - 4$ (h) $10t + 4u - 7t - 3u$

> *Example:*
> $4a + 3b + 5a - b$
> $= 4a + 5a + 3b - b$
> $= 9a + 2b$

2 Simplify these expressions by collecting like terms.

(a) $5x + 4y + x - 6y$ (b) $3k - 7 + k - 4$

(c) $7g - 4h - 6g + 5h$ (d) $6z + 4w - 8z - w$

3 Write expressions for the perimeter of these shapes. Write each expression in its simplest form.

> To work out the perimeter of a shape, you need to add together the lengths of all its sides.

(a) A square, side $2x + 3$.   ⬜ $2x + 3$

(b) A rectangle, length $3a + 2$ and width $2b - 1$. $2b - 1$ $3a + 2$

4 Simplify these expressions.

(a) $4j + 3k + j + 5l + 2k + 3l$

(b) $v + 6 + 7v + 2v - 5 + v$

(c) $8x + 5y + 6z - 3x + y - 4z$

(d) $7a - 3b - 6a + 9c - 4b - 5c$

5 Simplify these expressions.

  (a) $2xy + 5x + 4xy - 3x$ (b) $a^2 + 2a + 4a^2 + 3a$

  (c) $4t^2 + 3 + t^2 - 5 - 2t^2$ (d) $5jk + 7j + 2k + 4j - 3jk - 6k$

> xy and x are not like terms.
> a^2 and a are not like terms.
> Remember that $a^2 = 1a^2$.

6 Copy and complete the magic square.

		$3x + 3y$
	$5x + 2y + z$	$4x + 4y - z$
		$8x - y + 4z$

Exercise 4iv

Links: 4D–G

What you should know

To multiply algebraic terms, multiply the numbers first and then multiply the letters.

When you expand brackets you must multiply each term inside the brackets by the term outside the brackets.

1 Simplify these expressions.

  (a) $5 \times 2a$ (b) $4 \times 4r$ (c) $3p \times 5$

  (d) $8v \times 3$ (e) $5 \times 7x$ (f) $4a \times 6b$

  (g) $9m \times 6n$ (h) $7f \times 6g$ (i) $t \times 5u$

  (j) $3x \times 7x$ (k) $6r \times r$ (l) $8w \times 7w$

> *Examples:*
> $4j \times 3k = 12jk$
> $2x \times 5x = 10x^2$

2 Expand the brackets to find the value of these expressions.

  (a) $2(40 + 3)$ (b) $4(50 + 8)$

  (c) $6(30 - 2)$ (d) $7(60 - 4)$

> *Example:*
> $5(40 + 7) = 5 \times 40 + 5 \times 7$
> $\qquad\qquad = 200 + 35$
> $\qquad\qquad = 235$

3 Simplify the following by multiplying out the brackets.

  (a) $3(x + 4)$ (b) $5(d + 6)$ (c) $4(7 + t)$

  (d) $6(8 + y)$ (e) $7(r + v)$ (f) $2(p + q + r)$

> Expanding brackets, multiplying out brackets and removing brackets all mean the same thing.

4 Simplify the following by removing the brackets.

  (a) $4(z - 6)$ (b) $2(g - 9)$ (c) $7(7 - a)$

  (d) $-5(x + y)$ (e) $6(d + e - 3)$ (f) $8(p - q + r)$

> *Example:*
> $4(a + 3b) = 4a + 12b$

5 Expand the brackets in these expressions.

  (a) $2(3a + 4)$ (b) $3(5b + 1)$ (c) $-7(4c + 5)$

  (d) $4(x + 3y)$ (e) $8(2j + k - 3)$ (f) $-6(4m - 3n + r)$

  (g) $2(a^2 + 2a + 1)$ (h) $3(x^2 + 3x - 2)$ (i) $5(y^2 - 2y - 8)$

6 Remove the brackets from these expressions.

(a) $a(a + 4)$ (b) $r(r + 1)$ (c) $y(y - 5)$

(d) $g(4g + 3)$ (e) $t(2t - s)$ (f) $k(4k - l)$

(g) $2x(x + 5)$ (h) $3d(2d + e)$ (i) $5x(3x - 4y)$

> Remember that $a \times a = a^2$ and $a \times b = ab$.
>
> *Example:*
> $x(x - 3) = x^2 - 3x$

Exercise 4v

Links: 4H

What you should know

To add and subtract expressions with brackets you expand the brackets first, then collect like terms.

Expand and then simplify these expressions.

1 (a) $3(x + 5) + 2x + 7$ (b) $2(c + 4) + 5c + 1$

(c) $4(k + 3) - 3k + 8$ (d) $5(3z - 2) + 2z - 12$

2 (a) $4(a + 2) + 3(a + 5)$ (b) $2(h + 3) + 4(h + 5)$

(c) $2(j + 3) + 5(j + 1)$ (d) $5(b + 2) + 3(3b + 7)$

> *Example:*
> $4(2a + 3) + 2(a - 8)$
> $\quad = 8a + 12 + 2a - 16$
> $\quad = 10a - 4$

3 (a) $2(b + 6) + 2(b - 5)$ (b) $4(e - 2) + 3(e + 5)$

(c) $3(3s - 2) + 4(s + 4)$ (d) $6(2t - 4) + 5(2t - 3)$

> Multiply both terms in the second bracket by the negative number in front of the bracket.

4 (a) $7(a + 3) - 2(a + 4)$ (b) $4(x + 1) - 2(x + 2)$

(c) $5(2i - 1) - 3(i + 4)$ (d) $3(s + 4) - 4(2s + 3)$

> *Example:*
> $-2(x + 3) = -2x - 6$
> Remember that $(- \times -) = +$.

5 (a) $4(c + 4) - 2(c - 3)$ (b) $5(u + 3) - 4(u - 5)$

(c) $3(2b - 1) - 4(b + 4)$ (d) $6(e - 2) - 3(2e - 3)$

Exercise 4vi

Links: 4J

What you should know

Factorising an algebraic expression is the opposite of expanding the brackets.

Factorise these expressions.

1 (a) $2f + 10$ (b) $5g + 10$ (c) $3h + 9$

(d) $6i + 12$ (e) $7k + 7$ (f) $20 + 4j$

> *Examples:*
> $5a + 15 = 5(a + 3)$
> $b^2 - 4b = b(b - 4)$

2 (a) $4x - 12$ (b) $3y - 15$ (c) $2z - 12$

(d) $5r - 5$ (e) $4s - 24$ (f) $18 - 6t$

> Remember that $7 = 7 \times 1$.

3 (a) $r^2 + 5r$ (b) $a^2 + 2a$ (c) $d^2 - 8d$

(d) $i^2 + 4i$ (e) $u^2 - u$ (f) $4s - s^2$

> Remember that $r^2 = r \times r$.

4 (a) $6s + 8$ (b) $10q + 15$ (c) $12u - 9$

(d) $6 - 9a$ (e) $15 - 6r$ (f) $9e^2 + 24$

> Remember that $6s = 2 \times 3s$.

Exercise 4vii

What you should know

Use a grid method to multiply two brackets. Multiply each term in one bracket by each term in the other bracket.

Expand and simplify:

1 $(x + 7)(x + 3)$ **2** $(n + 1)(n + 8)$ **3** $(k + 5)(k + 6)$

4 $(y + 4)(y - 1)$ **5** $(j - 1)(j + 6)$ **6** $(a - 3)(a - 4)$

7 $(x + 7)(x - 7)$ **8** $(f - 7)(f - 8)$ **9** $(p + 4)(p - 9)$

10 $(q + 4)(q + 6)$ **11** $(b + 4)(b - 4)$ **12** $(t - 2)(t + 3)$

Example:
$(x + 2)(x + 5)$
$= x^2 + 5x + 2x + 10$
$= x^2 + 7x + 10$

Mixed Exercise

1 **(a)** Alex buys five apples at x pence each. Write an expression for the total cost in terms of x.

    (b) Alex also buys eight oranges at y pence each. Write down an expression for the total cost of the apples and oranges.

2 Simplify

    (a) $3a + 5b - a - 2b$ **(b)** $6g + 4h - 2g - 5h$

3 Multiply out

    (a) $5(t + 3)$ **(b)** $6(p - 7)$ **(c)** $w(w + 1)$

4 Expand and simplify

    (a) $4(2m - 3n) + 5(2m + n)$ **(b)** $3(2x + 1) - 4(x - 3)$

    (c) $(q + 4)(q + 6)$ **(d)** $(f - 5)(f + 7)$

5 Factorise

    (a) $6t + 18$ **(b)** $4y - 10$ **(c)** $w^2 + 3w$

Checklist

You should know how to...	Grade	For more help, look back at Student Book pages....
use letters to write and simplify expressions	F	93–99
collect like terms	F/E	99–103
expand brackets	D/C	103–108
factorise expressions	D/C	108–111
multiply two brackets.	C	112

5 Equations and inequalities

Exercise 5i

Links: 5A

What you should know

Solve equations by treating both sides of the equation in the same way. What you add or subtract to one side of an equation, you do the same to the other side.

1 Solve each equation to find the value of the letter.

(a) $x + 5 = 9$ (b) $y + 3 = 11$ (c) $d + 4 = 12$

(d) $e + 12 = 32$ (e) $n - 7 = 4$ (f) $t - 10 = 2$

(g) $p + 17 = 20$ (h) $k - 11 = 6$ (i) $8 + u = 13$

(j) $6 - v = 4$ (k) $30 + w = 90$ (l) $12 - f = 8$

(m) $a - 3 = 17$ (n) $15 - g = 8$ (o) $4 - h = 0$

> The solutions to the equations in this exercise may be positive or negative and whole numbers, fractions or decimals.

2 Find the value of the letter in each of these equations.

(a) $6 = t - 3$ (b) $22 = r + 6$ (c) $9 = x - 10$

(d) $12 = z + 11$ (e) $50 = 100 - t$ (f) $32 = 64 - u$

(g) $7 = p + 6$ (h) $19 = a - 7$ (i) $10 = c + 5$

> Write the letter on the left-hand side of the equals sign in your answers.

3 I think of a number then add 12. My answer is 17.
What is my number? Write an equation and solve it.

> Call the unknown number by a letter, say n.

4 In a packet of sweets there are ten extra sweets. If there are 42 sweets in the packet altogether, how many sweets were there in the original packet? Write an equation and solve it.

Exercise 5ii

Links: 5B

What you should know

If you multiply or divide by a number on one side of the equation, you must do the same to the other side.

1 Solve these equations.

(a) $6q = 12$ (b) $3t = 15$ (c) $5p = 30$

(d) $4x = 24$ (e) $7y = 28$ (f) $9u = 63$

(g) $11w = 33$ (h) $8b = 40$ (i) $16 = 4c$

(j) $25 = 5d$ (k) $32 = 4g$ (l) $100 = 25n$

(m) $80 = 20m$ (n) $21 = 3j$ (o) $5k = 150$

> Write the letter on the left-hand side of the equals sign in each case. Equations involving a multiplication can be *undone* by dividing both sides by the multiplication factor.

2 Find the value of the letter in each of these equations.

(a) $\frac{a}{3} = 4$ (b) $\frac{k}{2} = 10$ (c) $\frac{g}{6} = 4$

(d) $\frac{h}{11} = 2$ (e) $\frac{m}{8} = 5$ (f) $60 = \frac{n}{10}$

(g) $7 = \frac{x}{3}$ (h) $13 = \frac{y}{2}$ (i) $14 = \frac{u}{3}$

Equations involving a division can be be *undone* by multiplying both sides by the denominator (i.e. the value on the bottom of the fraction).

3 A radio station has eight sets of tickets to a concert to give away. If there are 56 tickets altogether, how many tickets are there in each set? Write an equation and solve it.

Remember to write the unknown letter on the left-hand side.

4 Sally shared her packet of 20 biscuits between herself and four friends. How many biscuits did they each receive? Write an equation and solve it.

5 A family win £300 prize in a local lottery. Each member of the family of six has an equal share of the winnings. How much does each receive? Write an equation and solve it.

Exercise 5iii

Links: 5C

What you should know

To solve some equations, two steps are necessary before the solution is found.

1 Solve these equations.

(a) $4a + 2 = 14$ (b) $3x + 4 = 10$ (c) $2m + 7 = 13$

(d) $7p - 3 = 11$ (e) $9y + 4 = 31$ (f) $5t - 8 = 12$

(g) $10v + 20 = 70$ (h) $50b - 75 = 25$ (i) $14d - 15 = 27$

Add or subtract before dividing both sides by the value in front of the unknown.

2 Find the value of the unknown letter in each equation.

(a) $\frac{u}{2} + 5 = 9$ (b) $\frac{h}{5} - 7 = 2$

(c) $\frac{x}{4} + 12 = 13$ (d) $\frac{a}{6} - 10 = 0$

(e) $6 + \frac{e}{3} = 8$ (f) $19 - \frac{g}{8} = 8$

Add or subtract before multiplying both sides by the value of the denominator.

3 Solve these equations.

(a) $\frac{3w - 3}{9} = 1$ (b) $\frac{10t + 6}{3} = 12$

(c) $\frac{11 + 4x}{5} = 11$ (d) $\frac{20 + 5c}{7} = 10$

(e) $\frac{7h - 22}{3} = 2$ (f) $\frac{8i - 20}{12} = 3$

Multiply first by the value of the denominator. Then add or subtract before dividing.

Exercise 5iv

Links: 5D

What you should know

To solve equations involving fractions or decimals, two steps may be necessary. Leave your answer as a mixed number or decimal.

1 Solve these equations. Leave each answer as a fraction.

    (a) $6s + 3 = 12$ **(b)** $3l + 2 = 6$ **(c)** $16m - 1 = 1$

    (d) $12q - 5 = 7$ **(e)** $7t - 5 = 3$ **(f)** $9y + 3 = 17$

    (g) $8a - 3 = 3$ **(h)** $5 + 24i = 20$ **(i)** $21j - 2 = 7$

    (j) $15k - 26 = 9$ **(k)** $4p + 5 = 8$ **(l)** $5b - 6 = 1$

    (m) $12x - 1 = 9$ **(n)** $17 + 36y = 35$ **(o)** $100c - 75 = 5$

> Give your answers as mixed numbers.

2 Solve these equations. Leave each answer as a decimal.

    (a) $8w - 6 = 4$ **(b)** $5e + 4 = 13$ **(c)** $5x - 11 = 7$

    (d) $10u - 5 = 3$ **(e)** $6g + 7 = 70$ **(f)** $8l + 16 = 17$

    (g) $5n - 11 = 30$ **(h)** $20s + 6 = 60$ **(i)** $12 + 4p = 15$

    (j) $10t - 8 = 13$ **(k)** $3 + 4a = 8$ **(l)** $5y - 7 = 1$

    (m) $2t - 2 = 9$ **(n)** $21 + 5d = 35$ **(o)** $50f - 70 = 5$

> Give your answers as decimals.

3 I think of a number, multiply it by 4 and add 9. My answer is 39. What is my number?

4 Sarah thinks of a number, multiplies it by 10 and subtracts 4. Shauna eventually guesses the correct answer to be 2. What number was Sarah using?

Exercise 5v

Links: 5E

What you should know

To solve equations involving negative values, collect the *unknowns* on one side of the equation, by adding or subtracting the values given, before solving the equation by treating both sides in the same way.

1 Solve these equations.

    (a) $4e + 15 = 3$ **(b)** $2y + 12 = 2$ **(c)** $8z + 20 = 4$

    (d) $2m + 30 = 6$ **(e)** $2x + 11 = 5$ **(f)** $5c + 45 = 5$

    (g) $6p + 50 = 8$ **(h)** $7n + 42 = 14$ **(i)** $9l + 180 = 90$

    (j) $3b + 40 = 7$ **(k)** $14 + 4d = 2$ **(l)** $6a - 4 = -16$

    (m) $5 + 5f = 0$ **(n)** $80 + 11g = 3$ **(o)** $2h - 7 = -13$

> All the solutions in this exercise have negative answers.

2 Find the value of the unknown letter in each equation.

(a) $\frac{m}{2} + 5 = 3$ (b) $\frac{c}{3} + 10 = 8$ (c) $\frac{f}{3} + 8 = 7$

(d) $\frac{h}{5} - 9 = -10$ (e) $\frac{n}{4} - 3 = -7$ (f) $\frac{x}{3} + 2 = -1$

(g) $\frac{a}{5} - 5 = -9$ (h) $\frac{e}{3} + 11 = 4$ (i) $\frac{g}{8} - 5 = -7$

(j) $\frac{b}{4} + 15 = 12$ (k) $7 + \frac{d}{5} = 4$ (l) $\frac{q}{4} - 5 = -8$

(m) $\frac{p}{3} - 2 = -10$ (n) $10 + \frac{r}{10} = 0$ (o) $41 + \frac{s}{20} = 1$

3 Tom thinks of a number, multiplies it by 3 and adds 17. His answer is 5. Write an equation for this puzzle. What was his original number?

4 Heather thinks of a number and divides it by 3 before adding 7. The answer is 2. Write an equation for this puzzle and from it find the number.

Exercise 5vi

Links: 5F

What you should know

When there are unknowns on both sides of the equation, collect like terms on one side of the equation only before solving. Often, more than two steps are involved.

1 Solve these equations.

(a) $2x + 7 = x + 10$ (b) $4t + 8 = 3t + 13$

(c) $6p + 4 = 3p + 34$ (d) $12a + 4 = 8a + 16$

(e) $5c - 10 = 2c + 2$ (f) $3i - 5 = i + 25$

(g) $8k - 18 = 4k + 6$ (h) $5n - 4 = 2n + 20$

(i) $13y - 4 = 7y + 2$ (j) $4c + 12 = c + 39$

> Always subtract the smaller value of the unknown from the larger value of the unknown as your first step.

2 Solve these equations.

(a) $5q + 5 = 2q - 4$ (b) $4a + 2 = 3a - 2$

(c) $15w + 10 = 12w + 7$ (d) $6d + 12 = 4d - 2$

(e) $3x + 20 = 2x + 10$ (f) $7m + 16 = 3m - 4$

(g) $12c + 18 = c - 4$ (h) $5t + 12 = 3t - 4$

(i) $9y + 21 = 6y - 6$ (j) $20p - 30 = 15p - 45$

3 Steve and Diane start with the same number. Steve multiplies the number by 6 and adds 2. Diane multiplies the number by 9 and subtracts 4. Their results are the same.

(a) Write an equation for this puzzle.

(b) What number did they both start with?

4 Shona thinks of a number, multiplies it by 3 and subtracts 8.
Her answer is twice the number she started with. Write an
equation for this puzzle and solve it to find the number.

Exercise 5vii

Links: 5G

> **What you should know**
>
> Always expand equations with brackets first, then collect like terms. Solve by treating both
> sides of the equation in the same way.

1 Solve the following equations.

   (a) $3(t + 2) = 18$ (b) $5(p − 3) = 20$ (c) $9(x + 4) = 63$

   (d) $7(a − 2) = 21$ (e) $4(y − 3) = 28$ (f) $10(c + 4) = 100$

   (g) $3(u + 5) = 3$ (h) $12(b + 4) = 36$ (i) $8(d + 5) = 24$

> Remember that
> $3(x + 2) = 3x + 6$

2 Find the value of the letter in each of these equations.

   (a) $5(2t + 2) = 30$ (b) $4(5y − 16) = 36$

   (c) $3(3p + 15) = 9$ (d) $11(11k − 13) = 220$

   (e) $8(2s + 14) = 16$ (f) $2(3m + 17) = 4$

   (g) $7(3x − 15) = 105$ (h) $6(3n − 10) = 48$

   (i) $10(6a + 6) = 300$ (j) $3(2w + 21) = 15$

3 Solve these equations.

   (a) $3(i + 3) = 2(2i + 3)$ (b) $4(2t + 3) = 2(5t + 1)$

   (c) $5(4a − 3) = 11(a − 3)$ (d) $9(2x + 1) = 3(5x + 6)$

   (e) $8(2h + 11) = 3(h + 12)$ (f) $20(9n + 2) = 7(15n − 5)$

   (g) $4(t + 7) = 11(2t − 4)$ (h) $15(q + 7) = 6(3q + 19)$

   (i) $15(3p − 20) = 2(7p + 5)$ (j) $100(20m − 5) = 25(65m − 35)$

4 Cath and Peter start with the same number. Cath adds 7 to the
number and then multiplies the answer by 3. Peter multiplies
the number by 8 and adds only 1. Cath and Peter end up with
the same answer.

   (a) Write an equation for this puzzle.

   (b) What was the original number?

5 I think of a number, multiply it by 3 and add 7. I then multiply
my answer by 4. I obtain the same answer if I multiply my
number by 7 and add 16 before multiplying this by 2.

   (a) Write an equation to show this puzzle.

   (b) Using the equation, work out the value of the number.

Exercise 5viii

Links: 5H

What you should know

An expression in which the left- and right-hand sides are not equal is called an inequality.

A number line can be used to show the solutions to an inequality using the symbols on the right.

The complete set of answers is the solution set.

$<$ means less than
$>$ means greater than
$\leqslant$ means less than or equal to
$\geqslant$ means greater than or equal to

o means less than or greater than
● means less than or equal to or greater than or equal to

1 Write the correct inequality between these pairs of numbers.

    (a) 4, 7   **(b)** $-6, -4$ **(c)** $-10, 45$

    (d) $-6, -13$ **(e)** 2.7, 2.6   **(f)** 19.45, 19.46

    (g) 0.010, 0.011   **(h)** 9989, 9998

    (i) 100 101, 100 110   **(j)** 10.0023, 10.1023

2 Write down the whole number values for each letter to make the inequality true.

    (a) $a > 4$ and $a < 7$ **(b)** $m < 6$ and $m \geqslant 1$

    (c) $x \leqslant 2$ and $x \geqslant -1$ **(d)** $p > 25$ and $p \leqslant 30$

    (e) $c \leqslant 0$ and $c \geqslant -4$ **(f)** $n > 100$ and $n \leqslant 101$

    (g) $r > -16$ and $r \leqslant -14$ **(h)** $t < -7$ and $t \geqslant -9$

    (i) $y \geqslant 1000$ and $y \leqslant 1006$ **(j)** $b < 1$ and $b \geqslant 0$

3 Write each pair of inequalities given in question 2 as a combined inequality.

4 Draw a number line between -5 and 10. Show the following inequalities on the number line.

    (a) $x \geqslant 4$ **(b)** $p \leqslant 9$ **(c)** $d > -3$

    (d) $s < 0$ **(e)** $-1 < j < 3$ **(f)** $8 < h \leqslant 10$

    (g) $-5 \leqslant a \leqslant -3$ **(h)** $-3 < b \leqslant 7$ **(i)** $2 < y < 4$

> Use the open and closed circles as the end points.

5 Write down the values for each letter to one decimal place to satisfy the inequality.

    (a) $f > 9.9$ and $f \leqslant 10.2$ **(b)** $m \leqslant 0.3$ and $m \geqslant 0.1$

    (c) $t \geqslant 99.9$ and $t \leqslant 100.2$ **(d)** $-5.1 \leqslant q < -4.7$

    (e) $-16.7 < h < -16.3$ **(f)** $-0.3 \leqslant n < 0.4$

Exercise 5ix

Links: 5I

> **What you should know**
>
> To solve equations involving inequalities, you use the same rules of algebra as ordinary equations and do the same to both sides.

1 Solve the following inequalities, where the letter has integer values.

(a) $4t > 28$ (b) $5x \leqslant 30$ (c) $10b \geqslant 80$ (d) $3c < -15$

(e) $7m \leqslant 56$ (f) $6a > -42$ (g) $8r \geqslant 24$ (h) $9w \leqslant -27$

(i) $21 \leqslant 3n$ (j) $-44 > 11u$

2 Solve the following inequalities, where the letter has integer values.

(a) $4h + 3 > 16$ (b) $7m - 3 > 32$ (c) $8 + 5y < 28$

(d) $9k + 20 > 2$ (e) $3j - 17 \geqslant 6$ (f) $15 + 2x \leqslant 1$

(g) $12p - 7 < 5$ (h) $5t + 19 > 4$ (i) $2q + 10 > 0$

3 Solve these double inequalities.

(a) $20 < 5q \leqslant 45$ (b) $21 \leqslant 3c \leqslant 36$

(c) $12 < 4x \leqslant 44$ (d) $0 \leqslant 9b \leqslant 54$

(e) $-8 < 8m \leqslant 48$ (f) $-18 \leqslant 6d < -12$

(g) $-121 \leqslant 11h \leqslant -55$ (h) $28 \leqslant 7a \leqslant 49$

(i) $0 < 2z < 3$

> Each unknown letter here represents a value or set of values.

Mixed Exercise

1 Solve each of these equations.

(a) $m + 4 = 7$ (b) $x - 5 = 6$ (c) $7 - a = 3$

(d) $16 = y + 9$ (e) $3 = p - 6$ (f) $8 = q - 5$

> The solutions to the equations may be positive, negative, whole numbers, fractions or decimals.

2 I think of a number then add 7. My answer is 26. What is my number? Write an equation and solve it.

3 Solve these equations.

(a) $5x = 35$ (b) $81 = 9y$ (c) $\dfrac{d}{4} = 8$

(d) $14 = \dfrac{q}{3}$ (e) $6d + 1 = 19$ (f) $17 - 3x = 11$

(g) $\dfrac{y}{3} + 4 = 7$ (h) $22 - \dfrac{h}{5} = 16$ (i) $\dfrac{6x - 2}{11} = 2$

(j) $7p + 2 = 6$ (k) $13 - 6s = 2$ (l) $4f - 23 = 3$

(m) $9 + 6i = 18$ (n) $2t + 9 = 1$ (o) $22 + 7h = 8$

(p) $\dfrac{d}{3} + 4 = 2$ (q) $5 - \dfrac{y}{4} = 7$

4 Solve these equations.

(a) $3c + 4 = 4c - 2$ (b) $4s + 10 = 3s + 8$

(c) $2(r + 3) = 16$ (d) $6(3p - 7) = 30$

(e) $3(4x - 2) = 9(2x - 1)$

5 Write the inequalities between these pairs of numbers.

(a) 20, 28   (b) 0.5, 0.4   (c) $-16, -8$

6 Write down the whole number values for each letter.

(a) $y > 10$ and $y \leqslant 13$ (b) $d \leqslant -1$ and $d > -4$

7 Draw a number line to show the following inequalities.

(a) $-2 \leqslant t < 5$ (b) $6 < d < 10$ (c) $0 \leqslant f < 3$

8 Solve the following inequalities.

(a) $3g \geqslant 18$ (b) $-21 \leqslant 7t$ (c) $3c - 6 \leqslant 9$

(d) $20 < 4j \leqslant 36$ (e) $-8 \leqslant 8k \leqslant 64$

Checklist

You should know how to...	Grade	For more help, look back at Student Book pages...
solve simple equations by treating both sides in the same way	F	115–121
deal with equations that have negative, decimals or fractional answers	D/C	121–123
solve equations combining two or more operations or involving brackets	E to C	123–126
write inequalities and represent them on a number line	C	126–128
solve simple inequalities and find the solution set.	C	129–131

Exercise 6i

Links: 6A–C

> ### What you should know
>
> Describe angles by the amount of turn, three letters, a number of degrees, or the type of angle: acute, right angle, straight line, obtuse or reflex.

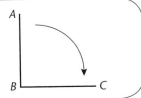

1 Describe the turn a minute hand of a clock makes between
  (a) 9.15 AM and 9.30 AM   **(b)** 2 PM and 2.45 PM.

2 For each of the following angles
  (i)   describe the angle using three letters and say whether it is acute, right-angled, a straight line, obtuse or reflex
  (ii) measure the angle in degrees.

(a)   **(b)**

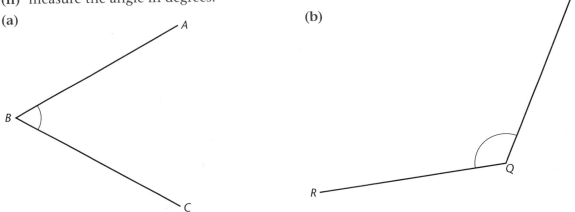

(c)

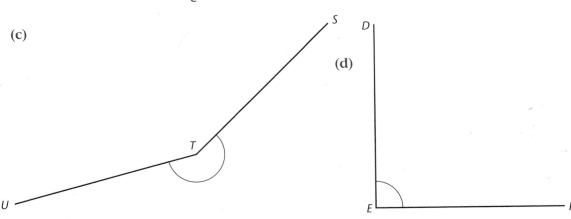

  (d)

3 Draw the following angles using a protractor and label the angle with the letters given.
  (a) angle $PTV = 75°$ **(b)** angle $SUT = 300°$

Exercise 6ii

Links: 6D, 6E

What you should know

Angles on a straight line add up to 180°.

Angles around a point add up to 360°.

Alternate angles are equal.

Vertically opposite angles are equal.

Corresponding angles are equal.

Co-interior angles add up to 180°.

1 Calculate the size of the angles marked with letters.
Give the angle facts you used to find your answers.

(a)

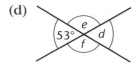

120° a

(b)

50°
60°
b
75° 110°

(c)

18°
c

(d)

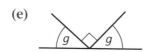

e
53° d
f

(e)

g   g

(f)

h 3h 2h

2 Calculate the size of the angles marked with letters.
Give the angle facts you used to find your answers.

(a)

48°
a

(b)

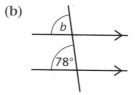

b
78°

(c)

c
62°

(d)

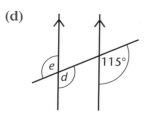

e
d 115°

(e)

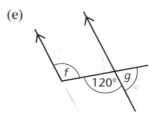

f
120° g

(f)

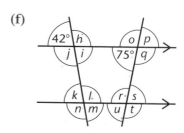

42° h   o p
j i   75° q
k l.   r s
n m   u t

Exercise 6iii

What you should know

Bearings are measured from the north in a clockwise direction.

Bearings have three digits.

1 For each diagram

  (i) write down the bearing of *T* from *R*

  (ii) work out the bearing of *R* from *T*.

(a)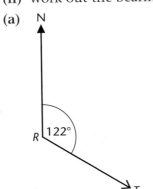

(b)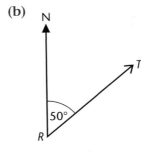

(c)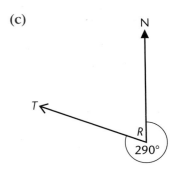

2 Draw accurate diagrams to show these three-figure bearings.

  (a) 080°   **(b)** 165°   **(c)** 264°   **(d)** 308°

3 Use a protractor to measure the following bearings:

  (a) *B* from *A*   **(b)** *C* from *B*   **(c)** *C* from *D*

  (d) *E* from *D*   **(e)** *A* from *E*   **(f)** *E* from *A*

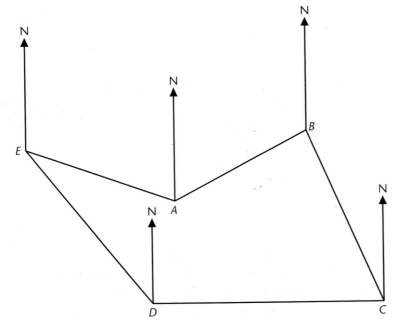

Exercise 6iv

Links: 6G, 6H

What you should know

Scalene, isosceles, equilateral and right-angled are the
four types of triangle.

Angles in a triangle add up to 180°.

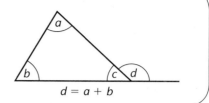

$d = a + b$

1 Sketch an example of the following types of triangle, showing
their main properties.

(a) right-angled   (b) isosceles

(c) equilateral   (d) scalene

2 Calculate the size of the angles marked with letters in the diagram.

(a)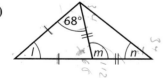

(b)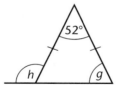

(c)

(d)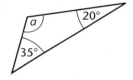

(e)

(f)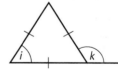

180
−48

132

(g)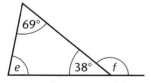

(h)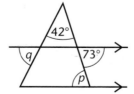

(i)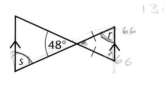

66   6

66

Exercise 6v

Links: 6I

What you should know

Square, rectangle, parallelogram, rhombus, trapezium and kite are special quadrilaterals.
Quadrilaterals are four-sided polygons. The interior angles add up to 360°.

1 For each pair of quadrilaterals
   (i) name the two shapes
   (ii) say which properties are the same
   (iii) say which properties are different.

(a)

(b)

(c)

(d)

2 Write down the names of all the quadrilaterals that have
   (a) diagonals that bisect each other
   (b) diagonals that bisect each other at right angles
   (c) only one pair of parallel lines
   (d) only one pair of opposite angles that is equal.

Exercise 6vi

Links: 6J

What you should know

The sum of the exterior angles of any polygon is 360°.

The sum of the interior angles is equal to $(n - 2) \times 180°$, where n is the number of sides.

A polygon can be split into two less triangles than the number of sides. The sum of the angles in each triangle = 180°.

For regular polygons, exterior angle = $\dfrac{360°}{\text{number of sides}}$.

> Polygons with all of the sides the same length and all of the angles equal are called *regular* polygons.

1 Calculate the size of the angles marked with letters in the diagram.

(a)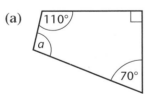

(b)

(c)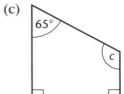

(d)

(e)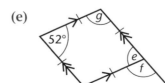

(f)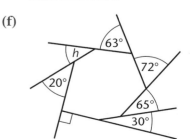

2 For a 12-sided regular polygon, find

    (a) the size of an exterior angle   **(b)** the size of an interior angle.

3 What is the sum of the interior angles of a 16-sided polygon?

4 How many sides does a regular polygon have if the exterior angles are 30°?

Exercise 6vii

Links: 6K, 6L

What you should know

A line of symmetry divides a shape into two halves. One half is the mirror image of the other.

A shape has rotational symmetry if it can be rotated to fit exactly onto its original shape.

1 Copy these shapes and draw in all the lines of symmetry (if any).

    (a)   **(b)**   **(c)**

2 Copy and complete these grids so that they are symmetrical along the dashed line.

    (a) 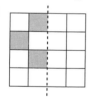   **(b)**   **(c)**

3 What is the order of rotational symmetry for each of the following shapes?

    (a)   **(b)**    **(c)**

4 Copy and complete this grid so that it has a rotational symmetry of **(a)** order 2 **(b)** order 4.

5 Draw shapes with the following orders of rotational symmetry.

    (a) 2   **(b)** 3   **(c)** 4

Mixed Exercise

1 Look at a compass to help describe the turn from

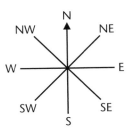

   (a) N to E **(b)** SE to NW **(c)** N to W.

2 Draw examples of the following angles and label them:

   (a) acute, *ABC* **(b)** obtuse, *PQR* **(c)** reflex, *STU*

3 Measure the angles you have drawn in question 2.

4 Calculate the size of the angles marked with letters in the diagram.

   (a) 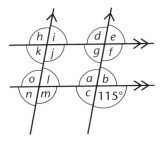 **(b)** 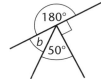 **(c)**

5 Calculate the size of the angles marked with letters in the diagram.

   (a)  **(b)**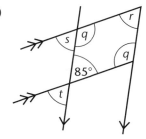

6 The diagram shows a triangle, *ABC*. Use a protractor to measure these bearings.

   (a) *B* from *A* **(b)** *C* from *B* **(c)** *B* from *C* **(d)** *A* from *C*

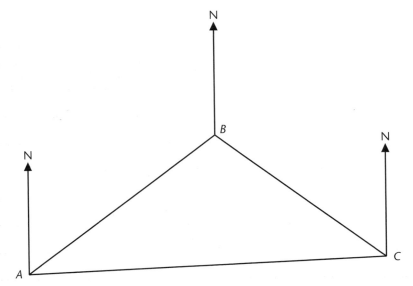

7 Calculate the size of the angles marked with a letter in the diagram.
For **(a)**, **(b)** and **(c)**, name the type of triangle shown.

(a) 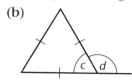 **(b)** 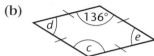 **(c)** 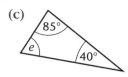 **(d)**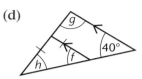

8 Calculate the size of the angles marked with letters in the
diagram. Name the quadrilateral in **(a)**, **(b)** and **(c)**.

(a) 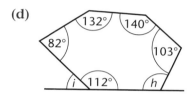 **(b)** 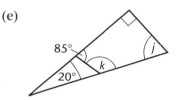 **(c)**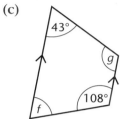

(d)  **(e)**

9 Copy each shape and mark on any lines of symmetry. State
the order of rotational symmetry.

(a) **(b)** **(c)**

Checklist

You should know about...	Grade	For more help, look back at Student Book pages...
describing and measuring angles	G	133–139
angle properties for points, lines and parallel lines	F to D	139–143
three-figure bearings	E/D	143–145
angles and triangles	E	146–151
quadrilaterals	E/D	151–153
polygons	E to C	154–158
symmetry.	G to E	159–162

7 Indices and formulae

Algebra 3

Exercise 7i

Links: 7A, 7B

> **What you should know**
>
> To use index notation, multiply the numbers first and then each letter in turn.

1 Write these expressions using index notation.

(a) $x \times x \times x \times x$

(b) $j \times j \times j \times j \times j \times j$

(c) $m \times m$

(d) $l \times l \times l \times l \times l \times l \times l \times l$

(e) $u \times u \times u \times u \times u$

(f) $p \times p \times p \times p$

Example:
$y \times y \times y \times y = y^4$

2 Simplify these expressions using index notation.

(a) $7 \times u \times u \times u$

(b) $n \times 5 \times n \times n \times n$

(c) $i \times 2 \times 3 \times i \times i$

(d) $t \times 4 \times t \times 3 \times t \times t \times t$

(e) $e \times 5 \times 1 \times e \times 2$

(f) $7 \times d \times d \times 7 \times d \times d$

Example:
$5 \times a \times a \times 4 \times a = 20a^3$

3 Simplify these expressions.

(a) $a \times a \times b \times b \times b$

(b) $p \times p \times p \times p \times q \times q \times q$

(c) $r \times t \times r \times r \times t$

(d) $4 \times x \times x \times 2 \times y \times y \times y$

(e) $c \times d \times 6 \times c \times d$

(f) $5 \times g \times g \times 3 \times h \times g$

Example:
$g \times g \times h \times h \times h = g^2 h^3$

4 Simplify these algebraic expressions.

(a) $2f \times 3f$

(b) $4x \times 6x$

(c) $3m \times 4m \times 2m$

(d) $2x \times x \times 7x$

(e) $4i \times i \times 2j \times 3j$

(f) $5t \times t \times t \times 3v \times v$

Example:
$6x \times x \times 3y = 18x^2 y$

Exercise 7ii

Links: 7C

> **What you should know**
>
> The laws of indices are
>
> $x^m \times x^n = x^{m+n}$ $\qquad x^m \div x^n = x^{m-n}$ $\qquad x = x^1$

Simplify each of the following:

1 (a) $a^2 \times a^3$

(b) $p^2 \times p^4$

(c) $t^5 \times t^3$

(d) $k^4 \times k$

(e) $r \times r^6$

(f) $x^3 \times x^5$

(g) $g \times g^7$

(h) $y^2 \times y^2$

(i) $c^3 \times c^3$

Example:
$x^3 \times x^4 = x^{3+4} = x^7$

2 (a) $a^5 \div a^3$

(b) $m^6 \div m^2$

(c) $b^5 \div b^2$

(d) $h^4 \div h$

(e) $r^4 \div r^3$

(f) $j^3 \div j^3$

Example:
$x^5 \div x^2 = x^{5-2} = x^3$

3 (a) $d^2 \times d^4 \times d^3$ (b) $x^5 \times x \times x^2$ (c) $z \times z^2 \times z^3$

   (d) $5n^4 \times 3n^2$ (e) $2f^3 \times 6f^4$ (f) $3y \times 7y^2$

> Multiply the numbers first and then multiply the letters.

4 (a) $4x^5 \div x^3$ (b) $10a^4 \div 2a^2$ (c) $3t^2 \div t^4$

> You can have negative powers.

5 (a) $\dfrac{a^3 \times a^4}{a^5}$ (b) $\dfrac{e^5 \times e}{e^3}$ (c) $\dfrac{4n^2 \times 2n}{n^2}$

> Simplify the top first and then do the division.

   (d) $\dfrac{3x^4 \times 4x^2}{6x^5}$ (e) $\dfrac{t \times t^3}{t^5}$ (f) $\dfrac{4k^3 \times 3k^4}{2k^3 \times 3k^2}$

Exercise 7iii

Links: 7D, 7E

What you should know

A formula is a general rule that shows the relationship between quantities that can vary. You can use letters for the variables in a formula.

1 To work out her pay, Emma uses the formula:

   pay = hours worked × rate of pay + bonus

   (a) What is her pay when she works ten hours at a rate of £7.25 per hour, with a bonus of £8?

   (b) What is her pay when she works 12 hours at a rate of £7.50 per hour, with a bonus of £6?

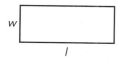

2 The formula for the area of a rectangle is $A = lw$, where l is the length and w is the width. Work out the value of A when

   (a) $l = 6$ and $w = 4$ (b) $l = 8$ and $w = 7$

   (c) $l = 12$ and $w = 9$ (d) $l = 13$ and $w = 11$

3 The formula for the area of a triangle is $A = \frac{1}{2}bh$, where b is the base and h is the height. Work out the value of A when

   (a) $b = 6$ and $h = 4$ (b) $b = 10$ and $h = 7$

   (c) $b = 7$ and $h = 8$ (d) $b = 9$ and $h = 5$

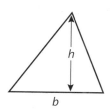

4 Use the formula $P = 2l + 2w$ to work out

   (a) P, when $l = 6$ and $w = 4$

   (b) P, when $l = 8$ and $w = 5$

   (c) l, when $P = 32$ and $w = 7$

   (d) w, when $P = 22$ and $l = 8$

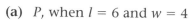
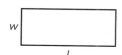

Exercise 7iv

Links: 7G, 7H

What you should know

Use the correct order of operations to help you do the calculations when you substitute values into an algebraic expression.

1 If $a = 5$, $b = 7$ and $c = 3$, find the value of these expressions.   Remember that $3a = 3 \times a$.

   (a) $a + b$ **(b)** $b + c$ **(c)** $b - 2$ **(d)** $3a$

   (e) $2b$ **(f)** $5c$ **(g)** $a + b + c$ **(h)** $a + b - c$

   (i) $5a + 6$ **(j)** $3b + 6$ **(k)** $4c - 7$

2 If $f = 4$, $g = 2$ and $h = 9$, find the value of these expressions.

   (a) $2f + h$ **(b)** $3g + f$ **(c)** $6f - h$ **(d)** $3g + 2h$

   (e) $5f + 8g$ **(f)** $3h - 2f$ **(g)** $3f - 4g$ **(h)** $5h - 4f$

   (i) fg **(j)** $gh + f$ **(k)** $fh - 5g$ $fg = f \times g$

3 If $r = 6$, $s = \frac{1}{2}$ and $t = -3$, find the value of these expressions.

   (a) $3r$ **(b)** $2s$ **(c)** $5t$ **(d)** $4r + 8$

   (e) $6s - 1$ **(f)** $5r + 4t$ **(g)** $2r + 5s$ **(h)** $4r - 2t + 4s$

4 If $x = 4$, $y = 2.5$ and $z = -2$, find the value of these expressions.

   (a) $3y$ **(b)** $5z$ **(c)** $x + y$ **(d)** $y + z$

   (e) $4x + 3z$ **(f)** $5x - 4y$ **(g)** $xy + 2z$ **(h)** $6x + 2y + 3z$

Exercise 7v

Links: 7I

What you should know

You can substitute values into expressions involving brackets and powers (indices).

1 If $a = 4$, $b = 6$ and $c = 5$, find the value of these expressions.

   (a) $\dfrac{a + 8}{2}$ **(b)** $\dfrac{c + 4}{3}$ **(c)** $\dfrac{b - 2}{2}$

   (d) $3a^2 + 1$ **(e)** $2c^2 - 7$ **(f)** $b^2 + 2a$ $3a^2 = 3 \times a^2 = 3 \times a \times a$

   (g) $3(4c + 2)$ **(h)** $a(b - 1)$ **(i)** $c(3b - 2a)$ Order of operations: brackets first.

   (j) $\dfrac{3b + 2}{a}$ **(k)** $\dfrac{8c - 4}{b}$ **(l)** $\dfrac{4c + 2b}{a}$

2 Copy and complete these tables.

(a)

x	1	2	3	4	5
$x^2 + 3x$			18		

(b)

x	5	6	5.5	5.7	5.8
$x^3 + x$		222			

Exercise 7vi

Links: 7J, 7K

What you should know

You can substitute values into a formula to work out the value of a variable.

The subject of a formula is always the letter on its own on one side of the equation. This letter only appears once in the formula.

You can rearrange a formula to make a different variable the subject.

1 A formula for the perimeter of a rectangle is
$$P = 2(l + w)$$
(a) Find the value of P, when $l = 7$ and $w = 5$.
(b) Find the value of P, when $l = 11$ and $w = 8$.
(c) Find the value of l, when $P = 26$ and $w = 4$.

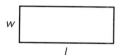

2 The formula for the area of a trapezium is
$$A = \tfrac{1}{2}(a + b)h$$
(a) Find the value of A, when $a = 9$, $b = 5$, $h = 3$.
(b) Find the value of A, when $a = 12$, $b = 8$, $h = 6$.
(c) Find the value of h, when $A = 40$, $a = 6$, $b = 4$.

3 Rearrange each of these formulae to make t the subject.
(a) $d = t + 5$ (b) $h = t - 8$ (c) $r = 4 + t$
(d) $f = 3t$ (e) $k = 5t$ (f) $v = at$

4 Rearrange each of these formulae to make x the subject.
(a) $y = 2x + 5$ (b) $y = 3x - 2$
(c) $y = 6 + 2x$ (d) $y = 7 - 5x$

5 Rearrange each of these formulae to make r the subject.
(a) $p = \tfrac{1}{2}r - 3$ (b) $q = \tfrac{1}{3}r + 5$
(c) $t = 2(r + 7)$ (d) $u = 4(r + s)$

6 The formula for the area of a trapezium is

$$A = \tfrac{1}{2}(a + b)h$$

> Remember that $\times \tfrac{1}{2}$ is the same as $\div 2$.

   (a) Rearrange the formula to make h the subject.

   (b) Rearrange the formula to make a the subject.

   (c) Rearrange the formula to make b the subject.

7 Rearrange each of these formulae to make x the subject.

   (a) $y = x^2$ (b) $y = x^2 - 1$ (c) $y = x^2 + 5$

   (d) $y = \dfrac{x^2}{3}$ (e) $y = \dfrac{x^2}{2} - 4$ (f) $y = \dfrac{x^2 + 1}{3}$

Exercise 7vii

Links: 7L

> ### What you should know
> You can use trial and improvement to find an approximate solution to an equation.

Use trial and improvement to find the solution, correct to one decimal place, for each of these equations.

1 $x^3 + x = 90$

   Copy and continue this table to help you.

x	$x^3 + x$	Comment
4	68	Too small
5		

2 $x^3 - 3x = 130$

> Use tables for questions 2–4.

3 $x^3 - 2x = 2$

4 $x^3 + x^2 = 500$

Mixed Exercise

1 Use the laws of indices to simplify the following equations.

   (a) $4x^2 \times x^3$ (b) $a^5 \div a^2$ (c) $12t^6 \div t^5$

2 A company uses this formula to find the cost, in pounds, of hiring a car:

   cost = 20 × number of days hire + 35

   (a) Calculate the cost of hiring a car for

   (i) three days   (ii) one week.

   (b) Rachel hires a car for a business trip. She pays the company £155. For how many days does she hire the car?

3 (a) Find the value of $4x + 6y$, when $x = 3$ and $y = 5$.

(b) Find the value of $5x + 3y$, when $x = 7$ and $y = -2$.

(c) Find the value of $3(x - 4y)$, when $x = 6$ and $y = \frac{1}{2}$.

4 Use the formula $v = u + at$ to find the value of v, when $u = -5$, $a = 6$ and $t = 1.5$.

5 Rearrange the formula $c = a + 5b$ to make b the subject.

6 Use trial and improvement to find the solution to the following equation.

$$x^3 + 3x = 200$$

Give your answer to one decimal place.

Checklist

You should know about...	Grade	For more help, look back at Student Book pages...
index notation	E	168–172
laws of indices	C	173–175
using formulae	G to C	175–179
substituting values into expressions and formulae	F to D	180–185
changing the subject of a formula	C	185–189
using trial and improvement.	C	189–191

Exercise 8i

Links: 8A–D

What you should know

Length, capacity and mass can be measured in metric or imperial units.
To estimate length, capacity and mass, compare with measurements you already know.

1   Write down a list of the *metric* units used to measure length,
    volume and mass. Put each set of units in order, from smallest
    to largest.

2   Write down a list, of the *imperial* units used to measure length,
    volume and mass.

3   Estimate the following. Give a metric answer and an imperial
    answer for each one.

    (a) The length of a pen.   **(b)** The volume of a spoon.

    (c) The height of a door.   **(d)** The mass of a bag of sugar.

4   For each statement, say whether the estimate is sensible.
    Give a better estimate where necessary.

    (a) Mr Wallis is about 250 cm tall.

    (b) A small car has a mass of about 200 kg.

    (c) The volume of a glass of milk is about 30 m*l*.

Exercise 8ii

Links: 8E, 8F

What you should know

To read a scale, look at how it's marked and the number of spaces between numbers.

1   What is the reading on the following scales?

    (a)   **(b)**   **(c)**

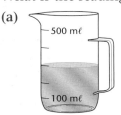

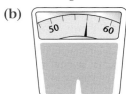

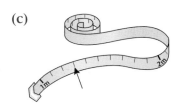

2 Copy the scales used in question 1 and mark on them

(a) 450 m*l*   (b) 53 kg   (c) 1.75 m.

3 Make a sensible estimate for each of the measurements shown.

(a)    (b) 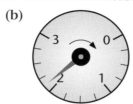   (c)

4 Copy the scales used in question 3 and mark on them

(a) 7.6 cm   (b) 1.8 units   (c) 2.43 PM.

Exercise 8iii

Links: 8G–I

What you should know

Write time as AM and PM time or using the 24-hour clock.

To work out dates, you need to know how many days there are in each month.

1 Change these times into 24-hour clock times.

(a) 4 PM   (b) 6.30 AM   (c) 12.45 AM   (d) 2.10 PM

Example:

7.30 PM = 1930 using the 24-hour clock.

2 Write these as AM or PM times.

(a) 0800   (b) 1500   (c) 2115   (d) 1120

Example:

1015 = 10.15 AM

3 Copy and complete the table.

25 minutes before	Time	35 minutes after
	1115	
	1422	
	2348	

4 I need to allow 1 h 40 mins to get to work. What time will I arrive if I leave home at

(a) 0730   (b) 0645   (c) 0625

5 Use the calendar to answer the following questions.

(a) Today is Wednesday 6th. What will be the date two weeks on Friday?

(b) I go on holiday on the 23rd. I need vaccinations 10 days before I go. What day of the week will this be?

(c) If it is the 14th today, what will be the date a week on Sunday?

Exercise 8iv

Links: 8J

What you should know

Timetables for buses (or trains) are usually written in columns.
Read the time the bus leaves each place in the row opposite the place name.

1 This is a bus timetable from Torpool to Moortown.

Torpool	0730	0750	0810	0830	0850
Marton	0748		0830	0855	0919
Elwick		0823	0847	0912	
Hart	0808	0832	0856		0940
Trimdon		0848	0913	0940	
Moortown	0845	0911	0935	1002	1010

(a) How often do the buses leave Torpool?

(b) What time does the 0810 from Torpool arrive in Hart?

(c) How long does the 0730 from Torpool take to get to Moortown?

(d) How long does the 0855 from Marton take to get to Trimdon?

(e) I arrive in Hart at 0856. What time did I leave Marton?

(f) Which bus has the quickest journey between Torpool and Moortown?

(g) I have an appointment in Moortown at 1015. It will take me 12 mins to walk from the bus station to my appointment. What bus should I catch from Torpool? Explain your answer.

Exercise 8v

Links: 8K, 8L

What you should know

To change from larger to smaller metric units you multiply.
To change from smaller to larger metric units you divide.

1 Change these lengths into the units given.

(a) 8 cm = ☐ mm

(b) 7 m = ☐ mm

(c) 3.5 km = ☐ m

(d) 225 cm = ☐ m

10 mm = 1 cm
100 cm = 1 m
1000 mm = 1 m
1000 m = 1 km

2 Change these weights into the units given.

(a) 6000 g = ☐ kg

(b) 5000 kg = ☐ t

(c) 9 kg = ☐ g

(d) 3.7 g = ☐ mg

> 1000 mg = 1 g
> 1000 g = 1 kg
> 1000 kg = 1 t

3 Change these capacities into the units given.

(a) 4*l* = ☐ ml

(b) 3400 ml = ☐ *l*

(c) 80 ml = ☐ cl

(d) 9.5 cl = ☐ ml

> 10 mℓ = 1 cℓ
> 100 cℓ = 1 ℓ
> 1000 mℓ = 1 ℓ

4 Put the following in order, from smallest to biggest.

625 cm   0.06 km   5900 mm   6.1 m

> Change all the measurements into metres first.

5 John has three packages. They have a mass of 5800 g, 0.05 t and 5.85 kg. Place them in order, from the heaviest to the lightest.

6 Two boxes of biscuits have the same price. One is marked 1875 g and the other 1.8 kg. Which one is the best value?

Exercise 8vi

Links: 8M

> **What you should know**
>
> 8 km = 5 miles   30 cm = 1 ft   1 kg = 2.2 lbs
> 1*l* = 1$\frac{3}{4}$ pts   4.5*l* = 1 gallon

1 Which is bigger?

(a) 1 km or 1 mile

(b) 1 lb or 1 kg

(c) 1*l* or 1 pt

> It helps to remember that 2.5 cm = 1 inch and 25 g = 1 ounce.

2 Change these into the units given.

(a) 30 miles = ☐ km

(b) 32 km = ☐ miles

(c) 5 inches = ☐ cm

(d) 20 cm = ☐ inches

3 Copy and complete the following:

(a) 6 kg = ☐ pounds

(b) 33 lbs = ☐ kg

4 Change these into the units given.

(a) 4*l* = ☐ pints

(b) 3.2 gallons = ☐ *l*

5 The distance from Whitby to Leeds is 82 miles. How many kilometres is this?

6 A horse has a mass of 340 lbs and a cow has a mass of 155 kg. Which one is the heaviest?

7 A recipe for batter has 8 ounces of flour, 3 ounces of butter and $\frac{1}{2}$ pint of water. Change these into metric measurements.

8 I need a fish tank that will hold $8\frac{1}{2}$ gallons of water. I have found one which will hold 37 *l*. Is it big enough?

Change them both to the same units.

Exercise 8vii

Links: 8N, 80

> **What you should know**
>
> 1 m = 100 cm, so 1 m² = 100 × 100 = 10 000 cm²
> 1 m³ = 100 × 100 × 100 = 1 000 000 cm³
>
> Measurement can be discrete or continuous. Continuous measurement to the nearest whole unit may be inaccurate by up to a half unit in either direction.

1 Copy and complete these conversions.

(a) $6\,\text{m}^2 = \square\,\text{cm}^2$ (b) $5000\,\text{cm}^2 = \square\,\text{m}^2$

2 Copy and complete these conversions.

(a) $5\,\text{m}^3 = \square\,\text{cm}^3$ (b) $4\,300\,000\,\text{cm}^3 = \square\,\text{m}^3$

3 Convert the following:

(a) $1\,\text{km}^2 = \square\,\text{m}^2$ (b) $1\,\text{cm}^2 = \square\,\text{mm}^2$

(c) $1\,\text{m}^3 = \square\,\text{mm}^3$ (d) $1\,\text{ft}^2 = \square$ square inches

4 These have been measured to the nearest whole unit. Write the range within which each measurement lies.

(a) 6 mm   (b) 23 c*l*

(c) 3 mins   (d) 42 kg

Example:
22 kg to the nearest kg means
21.5 kg ≤ mass < 22.5 kg.

5 A cat weighs 2.3 kg to the nearest gram. What is the range of its possible weight?

Change your measurements into grams first.

6 A forest covers a rectangle of 5 km by 4 km, measured to the nearest kilometre.

(a) What is the smallest possible area?

(b) What is the largest possible area? Give your answer in square metres.

Exercise 8viii

Links: 8P, 8Q

What you should know

$$\text{speed} = \frac{\text{distance}}{\text{time}}$$

$$\text{density} = \frac{\text{mass}}{\text{volume}}$$

1 I travelled 150 miles in four hours. What was my average speed?

> In this exercise give all answers to two decimal places where necessary.

2 How far will I fly if my plane travels for six hours at a speed of 600 km/h?

> Remember to give the units in your answer (e.g. mph).

3 How long will it take John to run 1500 m if he runs at a speed of 2 m/s. Give your answer in minutes.

4 Copy and complete this table.

Speed	Distance	Time
56 mph	140 miles	
68 km/h		3 h 15 mins
	58.2 miles	2 h 12 mins

5 What is the density of a piece of wood with a volume of 24 cm³ and a mass of 210 g?

> Your answer will be in g/cm³.

6 What is the mass of a stone block with a volume of 3.5 m³ and a density of 1250 kg/m³?

7 A block of foam measures 3 m by 2 m by 2 m. Foam has a density of 0.5 g/cm³. What is the mass of the foam block? Give your answer in kilograms.

> Find the volume in cm³ first.

Mixed Exercise

1 What would be the most appropriate metric and imperial unit for measuring the weight of a baby?

2 (a) Estimate the reading on this scale.
   (b) Copy the scale and mark on it 110 g.

3 I have an appointment at 6.30 PM. It will take me 1 h 25 mins on the bus and a further 12 mins walking. What time should I catch the bus?

Give your answer in 24-hour clock time.

4 A café decides to label its size of drinks in centilitres. A small cup was 300 ml, a medium was 0.5 l and a large was 725 ml. What will their new labels read?

5 A trailer has a mass of 1.3 t. It is carrying a cargo of 70 boxes each weighing 49.5 lbs. What is the total weight of the trailer and its load in tonnes?

6 Which is bigger $\frac{1}{2}$ mile or 820 m?

7 A picture is 12 cm by 8 cm, measured to the nearest centimetre. What is it's smallest possible area?

8 I travel 259 miles in $4\frac{1}{2}$ h. What is my speed?

9 Sugar has a density of 1.8 g/cm^3. What is the volume of a bag weighing 1.5 kg?

10 How long will it take to travel 144 miles at 60 mph?

Give your answer in hours and minutes.

Checklist

You should know how to...	Grade	For more help, look back at Student Book pages...
estimate measurements and read scales	G/F	195–202
read 24-hour clocks, calendars and timetables	G/E	202–210
convert between metric units	G/F	211–214
convert between metric and imperial units	F/E	215–217
convert area and volume units	D/C	217–219
accuracy of measurement	C	219–221
calculate compound measures.	D/C	221–226

Exercise 9i

Links: 9A

What you should know

perimeter of a rectangle $= 2l + 2w$

area of a rectangle
$= l \times w$

area of a parallelogram
$= b \times h$

area of a triangle
$= \frac{1}{2} \times b \times h$

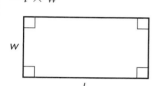

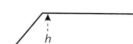

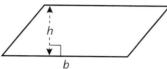

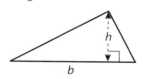

> Perimeter is the distance all round the outside of a shape.
>
> Area is the amount of space inside a shape.

1 Find the perimeter and area of the following shapes.

(a)

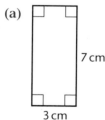

7 cm

3 cm

(b)

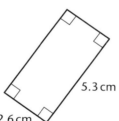

5.3 cm

2.6 cm

(c)

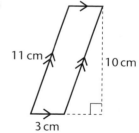

11 cm

10 cm

3 cm

(d)

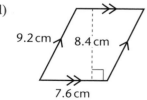

9.2 cm 8.4 cm

7.6 cm

(e)

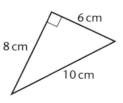

6 cm

8 cm

10 cm

(f)

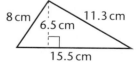

8 cm 11.3 cm

6.5 cm

15.5 cm

2 (a) Work out the area of triangle *ABC*.

(b) What do you know about the area of triangles *ABD* and *ABE*? Give a reason for your answer.

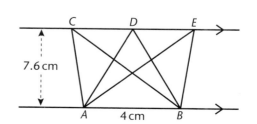

7.6 cm

4 cm

3 Draw a rectangle with an area of 24 cm² and a perimeter of 22 cm.

4 Both shapes have an area of 36 cm². Find the length of y in each case.

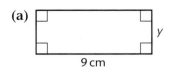

(a)

9 cm

(b)

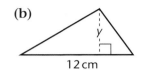

12 cm

Exercise 9ii

Links: 9B, 9C

What you should know

area of a trapezium $= \frac{1}{2} \times (a + b) \times h$
Areas of compound shapes are found by splitting the
shape into simple shapes and adding the areas together.

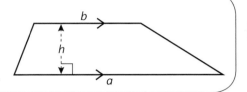

Area of trapezium $= \frac{1}{2} \times$ sum of parallel sides $\times$ perpendicular distance between them

1 Find the area of the following shapes.

(a)

5 cm
4 cm
7 cm

(b)

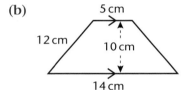

5 cm
12 cm
10 cm
14 cm

(c)

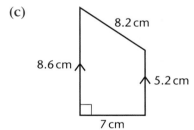

8.2 cm
8.6 cm
5.2 cm
7 cm

2 Find the areas of the following shapes by splitting them into simple shapes.

(a)

8 cm
2 cm
2 cm
2 cm

(b)

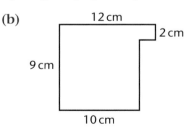

12 cm
2 cm
9 cm
10 cm

(c)

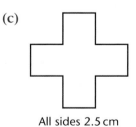

All sides 2.5 cm

(d)

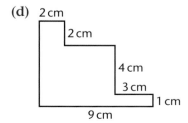

2 cm
2 cm
4 cm
3 cm
1 cm
9 cm

(e)

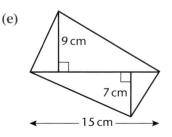

9 cm
7 cm
15 cm

(f)

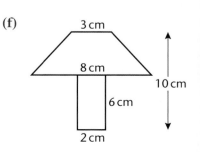

3 cm
8 cm
10 cm
6 cm
2 cm

(g)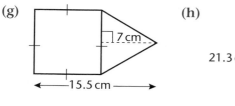

(h)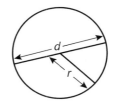

(i)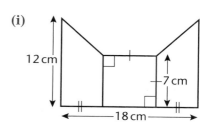

3 Find the perimeter of shapes **(a)**, **(b)** and **(c)** in question 2.

Exercise 9iii

Links: 9D, 9E

What you should know

circumference of a circle $= 2\pi r$ or πd

area of a circle $= \pi r^2$

1 Calculate the circumference of these circles, leaving your answer as a multiple of π.

  (a) diameter of 8 cm   **(b)** radius of 4.5 cm

2 Calculate the circumference of these circles, giving your answer to two decimal places.

  (a) diameter of 6 cm   **(b)** radius of 7.5 cm

3 A circle has a circumference of 15.4 cm. Find, to one decimal place, the circle's

  (a) diameter   **(b)** radius.

4 **(a)** Work out the circumference of this shape.

  (b) What is the perimeter of the full shape?

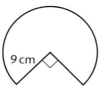

5 Calculate the area of the circles in question 1, leaving your answers as a multiple of π.

6 Calculate the area of the circles in question 2. Give your answers to three significant figures.

7 Work out the area of the shape in question 4.

8 A circle has an area of 380 cm^2. What is its radius?

9 Find the shaded area in each of the following:

(a)

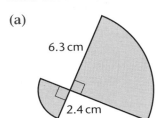

6.3 cm

2.4 cm

(b)

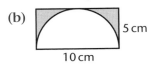

5 cm

10 cm

(c)

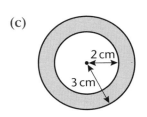

2 cm

3 cm

(d)

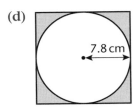

7.8 cm

Exercise 9iv

Links: 9F, 9G

What you should know

To draw a 3-dimensional (3-D) object on isometric paper, draw along the printed lines of the paper.

A plane of symmetry divides an object into two halves, where one half is the mirror image of the other.

1 On isometric paper, draw a 3-D diagram of
   (a) a cube with sides of 3 cm
   (b) two attached cubes with sides of 2 cm.

2 On isometric paper, draw 3-D diagrams of the objects with these cross-sections.

Use any value for the depth.

(a)

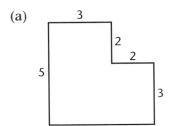

3

2

2

5

3

(b)

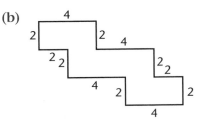

4

2

2

4

2

2

4

2

2

2

2

4

3 How many planes of symmetry are there in these objects?

(a)

(b)

(c)

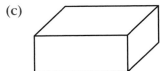

4 Copy this 3-D object onto squared paper.

Show all its planes of symmetry by drawing separate diagrams for each one.

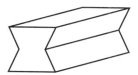

Exercise 9v

Links: 9H, 9I

> **What you should know**
>
> The net of a 3-D object is the 2-D shape that folds up to make the 3-D object.
>
> For a 3-D object: the plan view is from above
> the front elevation is the view from the front
> the side elevation is the view from the side.

1 Which of the following are nets of a cube?

(a)   **(b)**   **(c)**   **(d)**

2 Draw accurate nets of the following shapes.

(a)

3 cm
5 cm
7 cm

(b)

10 cm
4 cm

(c)

4 cm   5 cm
3 cm   6 cm

(d)

All sides 5 cm

3 For each of the following shapes, draw a plan view, a front elevation and a side elevation from the direction given.

(a)
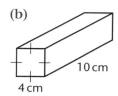

(b)
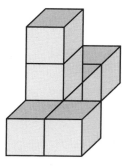

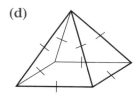
Plan
Side elevation
Front elevation

4 For the shapes in question 3, find
  (i) the volume   **(i)** the surface area.

Exercise 9vi

Links: 9K

> **What you should know**
>
> volume of a cuboid = $l \times w \times h$
>
> volume of a prism = area of cross-section $\times$ length

1 Find the volume of the following prisms.

(a)

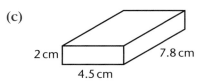

3 cm   9 cm

(b)

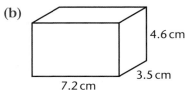

4.6 cm
3.5 cm
7.2 cm

A cuboid is a special type of prism.

A prism is a 3-D object whose cross-section is the same throughout its length.

(c)

2 cm   7.8 cm
4.5 cm

2 Find the volume of the following prisms:

(a)

5 cm
6 cm   14 cm

(b)

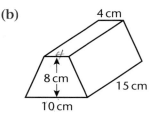

4 cm
8 cm
10 cm   15 cm

(c)

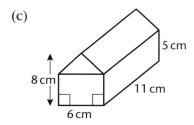

5 cm
8 cm   11 cm
6 cm

(d)

5 cm
12 cm   7 cm
23 cm
11 cm

3 A skip is filled to the top with mud.
What volume of mud will it hold?

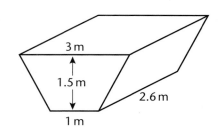

3 m
1.5 m
2.6 m
1 m

4 200 cm³ of metal is being recycled. It is made into a cuboid with a base that is 5 cm by 8 cm. What is the depth of the cuboid?

Exercise 9vii

Links: 9L

What you should know

Surface area of a cuboid = 2 × bottom + 2 × front + 2 × side or 2(*hw* + *hl* + *wl*)

To find the surface area of a prism, work out the area of each face and add them together. You can draw a net to help.

1 Work out the surface area of these cuboids.

(a)
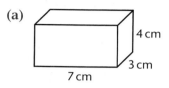
4 cm
3 cm
7 cm

(b)
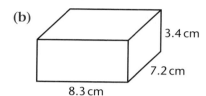
3.4 cm
7.2 cm
8.3 cm

(c)
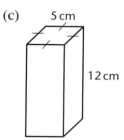
5 cm
12 cm

2 Find the surface area of these prisms.

(a)
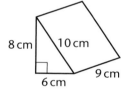
8 cm   10 cm
6 cm   9 cm

(b)
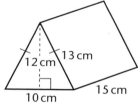
12 cm   13 cm
10 cm   15 cm

(c)
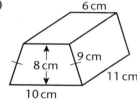
6 cm
8 cm   9 cm
10 cm   11 cm

3 John intends to paint his barn.

If 250 m*l* of paint covers 1 m², how much paint will he need?

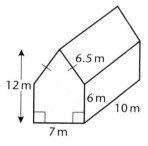
6.5 m
12 m
6 m
10 m
7 m

Exercise 9viii

Links: 9M

What you should know

volume of a cylinder = area of cross-section × height

1 Find the volume of these cylinders. Give your answers in terms of π.

(a) Base radius of 6 cm and height of 9 cm.

(b) Base diameter of 10 cm and height of 6.9 cm.

A cylinder is a prism with a circle as its cross-section.

$v = \pi r^2 h$

2 Find the capacity of a jar with a base radius of 3.5 cm and a height of 15 cm.

3 How much rain water can this piece of guttering hold?

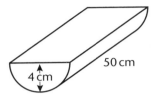

4 A cylinder has a volume of 314 cm³. The radius of the base of the cylinder is 5 cm. What is its height?

5 Jason is making solid metal ring doorstops to sell for charity. How much metal does each one need?

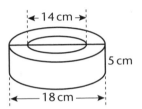

6 Water from a full rectangular tank that is 45 cm by 30 cm by 25 cm is to be put into a cylindrical drum. The height the water reaches in the drum is 60 cm. What is the radius of the drum? Give your answer to one decimal place.

Exercise 9ix

Links: 9N

> ### What you should know
>
> surface area of a cylinder $= 2\pi rh + 2\pi r^2 = 2\pi r(h + r)$
>
> total surface area of a cylinder = area of curved surface + area of each end

1 By first sketching a net, work out the surface area of the following cylinders.

(a)
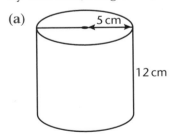

(b)
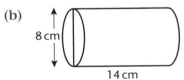

(c)
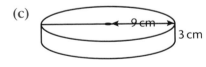

2 Jane has an open-topped cylinder plant pot. She wants to cover it with mosaic tiles. If it has a base diameter of 22 cm and a height of 24 cm, how many square centimetres of tiles should she buy?

3 Pipework for a chemical process has to be coated on all surfaces, inside and out, with aluminium. A joining piece 27 cm long has an outside diameter of 21 cm and an inside diameter of 13 cm. What is the area to be coated?

4 I have a piece of wrapping paper that is 40 cm by 60 cm. I want to use it to cover a cylinder with a radius of 8 cm and a height of 28 cm. Do I have enough paper to cover it with whole pieces of wrapping paper?

5 Sarah is painting a set of toy blocks. A set of blocks is made up of eight cubes that have a side length of 4 cm and eight cylinders that have a diameter of 4 cm and a height of 4 cm.

   (a) What is the surface area of one cylinder?

   (b) What is the surface area for the whole set of blocks?

   (c) A 25 m*l* tin of toy paint covers 300 cm². How many tins will be needed to paint the whole set?

Mixed Exercise

1 Find the perimeter and area for each of these shapes.

(a)
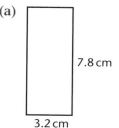
7.8 cm
3.2 cm

(b)
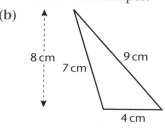
8 cm
7 cm
9 cm
4 cm

(c)
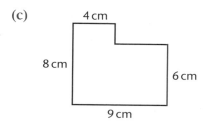
4 cm
8 cm
6 cm
9 cm

2 Find the area of the following shapes:

(a)
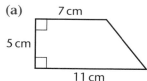
7 cm
5 cm
11 cm

(b)
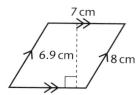
7 cm
6.9 cm
8 cm

(c)
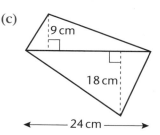
9 cm
18 cm
24 cm

3 Find the circumference and area of a circle that has a diameter of 17 cm. Give your answers as multiples of π.

4 Work out the perimeter and area of a running track that is made up of two semicircles joined together by two straight sections each of 120 m long. The radius of each semicircle is 28 m.

5 On isometric paper, draw a 3-D diagram with this cross-section. You can choose your own depth.

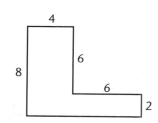
4
8
6
6
2

6 Draw this shape on squared paper and show all planes of symmetry. Draw a separate diagram for each plane of symmetry.

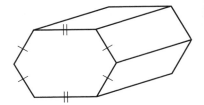

7 Draw the net of this shape.

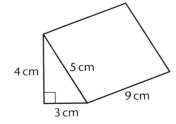

8 Work out the surface area of the shape in question 7.

9 Draw a plan view, a front elevation and a side elevation for this block of cubes.

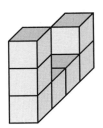

10 What are the volume and surface area of the 3-D shape in question 9?

11 Find the volumes of the following prisms:

(a)

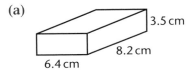

(b)

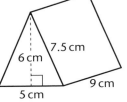

(c)

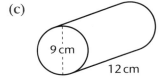

12 Find the surface area of each of the shapes in question 11.

Checklist

You should know about...	Grade	For more help, look back at Student Book pages...
perimeter and area of simple and compound shapes	F to D	232–242
circumference and area of a circle	D/C	242–249
drawing 3-D shapes and nets	G/F	250–251, 252–254
planes of symmetry	D	251–252
plans and elevations	D	255–257
volume and surface area of prisms	E to C	257–262
volume and surface area of cylinders.	C	262–267

Exercise 10i

Links: 10A

> **What you should know**
>
> Primary data is information you collect directly yourself.
>
> Secondary data is information you obtain from existing records.
>
> Qualitative data contains descriptive words.
>
> Quantitative data contains numbers.
>
> Discrete data only have particular values and is countable.
>
> Continuous data have any value in a particular range.

1 State whether each set of data is quantitative or qualitative.

    (a) The lengths of cars.   **(b)** Countries of residence.

    (c) Hair colours.   **(d)** Areas of rooms in a house.

    (e) Times recorded at a running event.

2 State whether each set of data is discrete or continuous.

    (a) The price of houses.   **(b)** Your mass.

    (c) Football scores.   **(d)** Page sizes.

    (e) The number of hours worked in a week.

3 State whether each source will give primary or secondary data.

    (a) A city centre survey.

    (b) The election results on TV.

    (c) Information found in a magazine.

    (d) Holiday information found on a website.

    (e) Your own questionnaire on school uniform.

4 How could you collect data on the following:

    (a) new and used car prices

    (b) types of mobile phones in the UK

    (c) weather forecast for your local area

    (d) local news stories?

Exercise 10ii

Links: 10B

> ### What you should know
>
> A table showing the tally marks and totals (frequency) is called a frequency table or frequency distribution.
>
> For a large amount of data, the results can be grouped together in class intervals. Between 5 and 10 class intervals can be used for either discrete or continuous data.
>
> When recording information, plan and prepare a data-capture sheet.

1 The number of visits made by a local district nurse during a typical working week is shown below.

8	5	11	4	9	7	7	2	0	10	6	7	8
5	1	3	0	6	5	9	10	12	10	5	1	8

Copy and complete the frequency table for this data.

Number of calls	Tally	Frequency
0–5		
6–10		
11–15		
	Total	

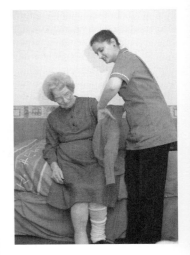

2 The amount of daily rainfall (in millimetres) recorded in a three-week period was as follows.

7	3	14	36	25	15	9	11	3	1	12
16	4	15	18	6	9	4	7	26	32	

Copy and complete the frequency distribution for this data. Use four equal class intervals.

Rainfall, r (mm)	Tally	Frequency
$0 \leq r < 10$		
$10 \leq r < 20$		
	Total	

3 The sizes of shoes sold in a shop during a busy Saturday period were recorded.

5	6	8	10	12	8	9	8	9	9	8	9	4	8
6	8	8	6	7	10	4	8	5	7	9	6	4	8
10	8	10	5	4	6	8	9	6	6	10	9	6	5
4	9	8	4	5	8	4	6	7	9	10	8	6	7
10	7	5	8	7	8	6	5	5	8	5			

Construct a frequency table for this data, showing the tally marks and frequencies. Use equal class intervals, beginning with 3−4 and 5−6.

4 The maximum daily temperature, t (°C), recorded by a local weather station during July is shown below.

19	19	20	22	24	25	25	24	25	22	20
20	19	17	17	18	21	22	22	19	16	14
14	14	18	20	22	24	25	26	26		

Construct a frequency table using six equal class intevals, beginning with $14 \leqslant t < 16$.

5 A survey is being conducted on the time spent using mobile phones. Construct a data-capture sheet to record this information for your class.

Exercise 10iii

Links: 10C

What you should know

A questionnaire is a survey that collects primary data.

A survey should test a theory or hypothesis.

Questionnaires should avoid asking personal questions and should be easy to complete.

1 Say whether each of these questions is suitable for a questionnaire. If you think not, explain why and offer a more suitable question to replace it.

(a) Do you agree that alcohol is bad for you?

(b) What type of sport do you like?

    (i) football   (ii) rugby   (iii) athletics   (iv) darts

(c) What type of films do you like watching?

    (i) horror   (ii) adventure   (iii) romantic   (iv) funny   (v) other

2 Design a questionnaire with up to six questions about the type of summer holidays your class takes. State your hypothesis before you start.

Exercise 10iv

Links: 10D

What you should know

Asking everyone in your survey is called the population.

Asking only a selection of your population is called a sample. Your sample should be representative of the population and this can be achieved by random sampling. If not chosen carefully, your sample could be biased.

1 *Most people in school like chips at lunchtime.* Describe how you would collect data to find out if this statement is true or false. You should include a questionnaire and explain how you would select your sample.

2 *Older people have smaller, newer cars.* Describe how you go about collecting information to test this hypothesis. Include information on how you would select your sample and what questions would be asked in your questionnaire.

3 *Shorter but more frequent school terms would help students learn.* How would you go about finding out if this is true or not. What questions would you ask in your questionnaire? How would you make sure that your sample was randomly chosen?

Exercise 10v

Links: 10E

What you should know

Two-way tables are similar to frequency tables but show two or more types of information at the same time.

1 In a survey of 25 adults, 10 out of 13 men asked said they prefer buying roses to carnations. Only eight women preferred buying carnations.
Copy and complete the two-way table to show this information.

	Roses	Carnations	Total
Men	10		
Women		8	
Total			

2 In an experiment on breathing, the following information about the percentages of gases was recorded.

Gas	Breathed in	Breathed out
Oxygen	21%	
Nitrogen		78%
Carbon dioxide		5%
Total	100%	

Copy and complete the table, using the knowledge that the amount of nitrogen breathed in and out is the same.

3 In a class of 32 pupils, 17 are girls. Bicycles are owned by 12 girls and 9 boys. Draw a two-way table to show this information.

4 Design a two-way table for your class to show the differences in hair and eye colours. Conduct the survey and record your results in the table.

Exercise 10vi

Links: 10F

> **What you should know**
>
> Both discrete and continuous data can be shown in a two-way table.

1 The two-way table shows the number of CDs owned by pupils in three classes in Year 10.

    (a) How many pupils are there in each class?

    (b) How many pupils in total own less than 20 CDs?

    (c) How many pupils in 10B and 10C own more than 9 but less than 30 CDs?

Number of CDs	10A	10B	10C
0–9	15	10	11
10–19	9	19	12
20–29	4	0	7
30–39	0	1	0
40+	2	0	0

2 The two-way table shows the number of patients seen by a group of local doctors and the time spent with each patient.

Time, t (mins)	Dr Mamood	Dr Rice	Dr Cummings
$0 \leqslant t < 3$	9	12	8
$3 \leqslant t < 6$	13	10	15
$6 \leqslant t < 9$	4	8	8
$9 \leqslant t < 12$	5	3	4
$12 \leqslant t < 15$	0	2	1

    (a) How many patients did Dr Rice see in total?

    (b) Which doctor saw the most patients?

    (c) How many patients were seen altogether?

    (d) How many patients in total waited less than six minutes?

Exercise 10vii

Links: 10G

> **What you should know**
>
> Two-way tables can also show different types of information, such as timetables and calendars.

1 The cost of car hire (£) in France can be found in the following table.
The minimum hire charge is for two days.

Car type	Number of days hire						Extra day
	2	3	4	5	6	7	
Clio	62	92	123	154	184	189	5
Megane	67	101	134	167	201	206	5
Renault Laguna	82	123	164	205	246	253	7
Vauxhall Omega	112	167	223	279	335	342	7
Espace	149	223	298	372	446	456	10

(a) What is the cost of hiring a Renault Laguna for four days?

(b) What is the cost of hiring a Vauxhall Omega for one day?

(c) Work out the cost of hiring an Espace for 15 days.

2 The cost of a River Explorer Cruise or combined River Explorer and Aquarium Cruise is shown in the table.

	River Explorer Cruise		plus Aquarium
	Single	Return	Return
Adult	2.40	4.65	5.50
Child (3−4 years of age)	Free	Free	1.20
Child (5−15 years of age)	1.35	2.60	3.40
Concession*	1.85	3.40	4.50
Family (2 adults and 3 children)		11.99	15.45

*Students and seniors (over 60 years of age)

(a) Work out the cost of a return River Explorer Cruise for three adults and three children (all over five years old).

(b) Is this cheaper than buying a family ticket plus one adult ticket? What is the difference?

(c) What is the cost for a return ticket for a senior with two grandchildren (aged four and seven years old, respectively) to visit the Aquarium on the River Explorer Cruise?

3 The table shows the repayments schedule for various loans over three different repayment periods. The amounts shown are the monthly repayments with financial protection.

Loan value	3 years	5 years	7 years
£3000	£108	£74	£60
£5000	£180	£123	£100
£10 000	£361	£246	£200
£15 000	£542	£369	£300

(a) What are the monthly repayments for an £8000 loan taken out over five years?

(b) How much money in total is repaid on a £20 000 loan taken out over seven years?

Mixed Exercise

1 For each measure, state whether the data is discrete or continuous.

  (a) kg   (b) mm   (c) size 10   (d) 3 acres

  (e) 67°   (f) 4 goals   (g) 15″ collar   (h) 2l

2 In a local fitness centre, the age of each member, a, entering the centre one morning was monitored.

    26 28 42 50 22 35 47 39 56 61
    64 48 51 27 31 52 59 46 33 27
    18 18 39 50 41 25 37 64 44 40

Using groups $10 \leqslant a < 20$ etc, construct a frequency table showing tally marks and frequencies.

3 A local community is conducting a survey about the number 191 bus service. Make a list of questions that perhaps should be considered in a questionnaire. Include ideas about who should be in the sample.

4 *The number 191 bus service should be discontinued.* Create a simple questionnaire that would help to answer this question.

5 This table shows the distances between various towns on the number 191 bus route.

Towns	Distance from Middlewood (km)
Middlewood	0
Poynton	3
Hazel Grove	6.5
Stepping Hill	7.5
Heaviley	9.5
Stockport	11.5

Copy and complete the two-way table below to show this information.

Middle Wood					
3	Poynton				
	3.5	Hazel Grove			
			Stepping Hill		
				Heaviley	
			4		Stockport

6 This is part of the bus timetable for the number 191 bus between Middlewood and Stockport.

Monday to Fridays		
Middlewood	0910	1022
Poynton	0922	1034
Hazel Grove	0929	1041
Stepping Hill	0934	1046
Heaviley	0939	1051
Stockport	0948	1100

(a) Look at the bus that departs Middlewood at 0910. What time does it arrive at Stepping Hill?

(b) How long does the journey between Hazel Grove and Stockport take?

(c) Phil arrives at the bus stop in Poynton at twenty-five past nine in the morning. How long does he need to wait for the next bus?

Checklist

You should know how to...	Grade	For more help, look back at Student Book pages...
identify different types of data	F	272–273
construct tally charts or frequency tables for discrete and grouped data	G to D	274–278
design a questionnaire and a data-capture sheet	D/C	276–280
select a representative sample	D/C	280–282
design and use two-way tables for discrete and grouped data.	E/D	282–291

Exercise 11i

Links: 11A

> **What you should know**
>
> A pictogram is a table containing a picture or symbol that represents an item or number of items.

1 The pictogram below shows the number of CDs owned by a group of friends.

Fiona owns six CDs and John owns 22 CDs.

(a) Complete the pictogram to show this information.

(b) How many CDs does the group own altogether?

Name	CDs
Sally	◉ ◉ ◉
Fiona	
Anwar	◉
John	
Shauna	◉ ◉

Key: ◉ represents four CDs.

2 The table below shows the number of times people from a particular country have won the Nobel prize for literature.

Country	Number of prizes awarded
Sweden	7
USA	10
France	12
UK	8
Norway	3

Draw a pictogram to represent these results. Use the symbol 📖 to represent two prizes.

3 This table shows the number of occasions some rugby league teams have won the challenge cup.

Draw a pictogram to represent these results.

Use the symbol ◗ to represent four wins.

Club	Wins
Castleford	4
Warrington	5
Wigan	16
Leeds	11
Widnes	7

Exercise 11ii

Links: 11B, 11C

> ## What you should know
>
> Bar charts and vertical line graphs show a pattern or trend in either qualitative or quantitative data. Bars of equal width can be drawn either vertically or horizontally.
>
> For qualitative or discrete data, gaps should be left between the bars. For continuous data, draw the bars with no gaps.
>
> Compound bar charts can be used to make comparisons between two or more sets of data.

1 The table shows the number of occasions the FA cup has been won by the top five league clubs.

Draw a bar chart to show this information.

Club	Wins
Liverpool	5
Newcastle United	6
Manchester United	11
Tottenham Hotspur	8
Arsenal	7

2 The table shows the average number of daily newspapers sold in the UK (in 2000).

Newspaper	Sales (millions)
The Daily Telegraph	1.1
The Mirror	2.4
The Express	1.1
The Sun	3.7
Daily Mail	2.3

Draw a vertical line graph to represent this information.

3 A box of old, mixed nails was sorted into nails of different lengths. The results are shown in the table.

(a) Draw a horizontal bar chart to represent this data.

(b) How many nails were in the box?

Nail length (inches)	Frequency
$\frac{1}{2}$	18
1	47
$1\frac{1}{2}$	12
2	21

4 The following bar chart shows the number of oranges and apples produced (in millions of tonnes) by six countries in 2005.

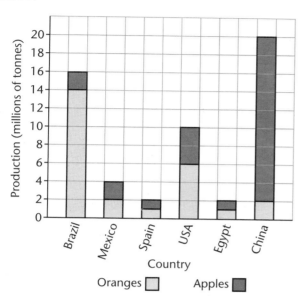

Use the bar chart to answer the following questions.

(a) How many millions of tonnes of **(i)** oranges **(ii)** apples were produced by the six countries altogether?

(b) Which country produced the most oranges? How many more tonnes did it produce than the total of the other 5 countries?

(c) Which country produced the most apples? How many more tonnes did it produce than the total of the other 5 countries?

5 The table below shows the results of a survey on the width of pupils' hand-spans.

Hand-span, w (cm)	Frequency
$15 \leqslant w < 17$	4
$17 \leqslant w < 19$	6
$19 \leqslant w < 21$	12
$21 \leqslant w < 23$	7
$23 \leqslant w < 25$	3

Draw a bar chart to show this information.

Exercise 11iii

Links: 11D

> ## What you should know
>
> Pie charts show how data are shared or divided. Each slice or sector of the pie chart represents the number of items out of the total number of items.
>
> Pie charts are not useful for reading off accurate information.

1. The number of different types of chocolate in a box of mixed chocolates are shown below.

Chocolate type	Number	Sector angle (°)
Dark	8	
Plain	10	
White	6	

   (a) How many chocolates were in the box (call this amount x)?

   (b) Now copy and complete the following sentence by replacing x with the value obtained in part (a):

   "x chocolates are represented by an angle of 360°. Therefore, one chocolate is represented by an angle of $\left(\frac{360}{x}\right)^{\circ} = \ldots^{\circ}$".

   (c) Now copy and complete the table, including the angle of each sector for each type of chocolate.

   (d) Draw a pie chart to represent this information.

2. In Morse code, each letter of the alphabet and the numbers 0−9 are represented by a series of dots and dashes. The table below shows the frequency that these occur.

Number of dots and dashes	Frequency	Sector angle (°)
1	2	
2	4	
3	8	
4	12	
5	10	

   (a) Work out the sector angle for each number of dots and dashes.

   (b) Copy and complete the table, including the sector angles.

   (c) Draw a pie chart to represent this information.

3 The pie chart shows the areas of four major oceans
(in millions of square miles).

By measuring the angles to the nearest degree, work out the
area of each of the oceans if the total area is 144 million
square miles.

Give your answer to the
nearest million square miles.

Exercise 11iv

Links: 11E

> **What you should know**
>
> Time series line graphs show trends in the data. You can only draw line graphs for
> continuous data where the plotted points are joined by straight lines or a continuous line.

1 In a science experiment, the current was measured through a
bulb as the voltage was increased. Here is the table of results.

Voltage, V (volts)	2	4	6	8	10	12
Current, I (amps)	1.8	2.8	3.5	4.1	4.6	5.0

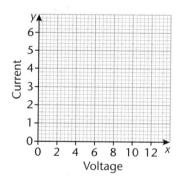

(a) Plot the line graph to show these results using the scales
shown.

(b) What was the approximate value of the current when the
voltage through the bulb was 7 volts?

2 The table shows the temperature of water in a kettle after it
was boiled and allowed to cool.

Time after boiling (mins)	0	2	4	6	8	10
Temperature (°C)	100	50	30	25	22	21

(a) Plot the graph of the results. Put 'Time after boiling' on
the x-axis, from 0 to 10, and put 'Temperature' on the
y-axis, from 0 to 100.

(b) What was the water temperature after three minutes?

3 The table shows the amount of snowfall that fell *each hour* during the night.

Time	2300	0000	0100	0200	0300	0400	0500
Snowfall (cm)	1	3	5	6	4	2	1

(a) Plot a graph to show this information. Use the y-axis to
indicate the amount of snowfall and the x-axis for the time.

(b) How much snow fell in total between 11 PM and 5 AM?

Convert from 24-hour
clock to AM/PM.

Exercise 11v

Links: 11F

> ### What you should know
>
> A stem-and-leaf-diagram keeps the original data, but also gives a picture of how the data is spread. A stem-and-leaf-diagram always has a key.

1 The maximum and minimum average monthly temperatures in Wellington, New Zealand, between January and December are shown below.

Max (°C)   20, 21, 20, 16, 14, 12, 11, 12, 13, 15, 17, 20

Min (°C)   13, 14, 12, 10, 8, 6, 5, 7, 8, 9, 10, 11

  (a) Copy and complete the stem-and-leaf-diagram for the maximum temperature, using the key 1|3 to represent 13°C.

  (b) Draw a similar stem-and-leaf-diagram to show the minimum temperatures.

2 In a typing test, the typing speeds (number of correct words/min) of 20 people were recorded.

    45, 56, 43, 48, 58, 63, 57, 56, 44, 54

    32, 46, 44, 60, 54, 61, 52, 49, 46, 55

Draw a stem-and-leaf-diagram to show this information. Include a key.

3 The hand-span data used in question 5 of Exercise 11ii are shown below.

    15.2, 15.8, 16.0, 16.4, 17.3, 17.4, 17.9, 18.1, 18.3, 18.7, 19.0,

    19.2, 19.2, 19.5, 19.9, 20.1, 20.1, 20.4, 20.7, 20.7, 20.8, 20.9,

    21.3, 21.5, 21.5, 21.6, 21.7, 21.8, 22.4, 23.0, 23.2, 24.3

Draw a stem-and-leaf diagram to show these results. Use the key 16|7 to represent 16.7 cm.

Exercise 11vi

Links: 11G

> ### What you should know
>
> Scatter graphs help to compare two sets of data, showing whether there is a connection or relationship between them. This relationship is called a correlation and is best seen in the line of best fit.
>
> Scatter graphs can have positive, negative or no correlation.

1 Here are five sketches of scatter diagrams.

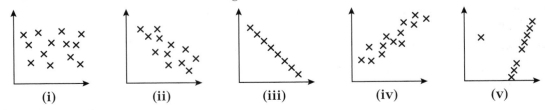

    (i)   (ii)   (iii)   (iv)   (v)

Which diagrams show

  (a) positive correlation   **(b)** negative correlation   **(c)** no correlation?

2 The table shows data from the first five planets in our solar system.

Planet	Average distance from the Sun (million km)	Time taken to orbit the Sun (years)
Mercury	58	0.2
Venus	108	0.6
Earth	150	1.0
Mars	228	1.9
Jupiter	778	11.9

(a) Plot the data for Mercury, Venus, Earth and Mars as a scatter diagram, using the scales shown.

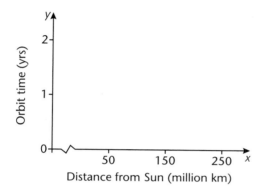

(b) Draw a line of best fit.

(c) Comment on the type of correlation found.

(d) How could you tell if the next planet (Jupiter) also fitted this trend?

3 The table below shows part of the results of a survey of university student behaviour.

Number of hours working	15	20	23	29	35	40	42	49	50
Number of hours watching TV	37	28	30	24	17	15	11	10	14

(a) Draw a scatter graph, using the scales shown.

(b) Draw a line of best fit.

(c) Comment on the type of correlation found.

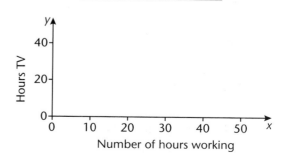

4 The table shows the number of road vehicles and the amount of road space per vehicle between 1980 and 1987.

Year	Number of vehicles (millions)	Road space per vehicle (m)
1980	19.2	17.7
1981	19.4	17.7
1982	19.8	17.4
1983	20.2	17.1
1984	20.8	16.7
1985	21.2	16.5
1986	21.7	16.2
1987	22.2	15.9

(a) Draw separate scatter graphs to show these results.

(b) Draw the line of best fit for both graphs.

(c) Comment on the type of correlation found.

(d) What would happen if this trend continued?

Exercise 11vii

Links: 11H

What you should know

Grouped data can be displayed in a frequency polygon. This is drawn from a bar chart, where the mid-point values of each bar (class interval) are joined by a straight line.

A frequency polygon shows patterns or trends in the data more easily than a bar chart.

1 Work out the mid-point values for each of the following class intervals.

(a) 20–30 cm (b) $10.8\ s \leqslant t < 11.4\ s$ (c) 300–350 ml

(d) $30\ mph \leqslant v < 40\ mph$ (e) $30\ g \leqslant m < 50\ g$

2 Copy these axes and draw a frequency polygon for this data.

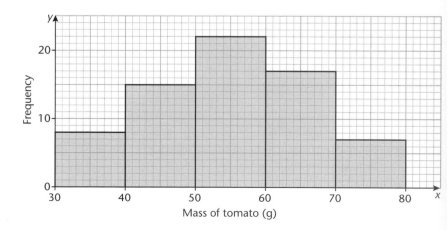

3 In a local golf club, the range of ages of all 185 members was recorded, as shown in the table.

Age, x (years)	Number of members	Mid-point value
$10 < x \leqslant 20$	13	
$20 < x \leqslant 30$	21	
$30 < x \leqslant 40$	42	
$40 < x \leqslant 50$	47	
$50 < x \leqslant 60$	31	
$60 < x \leqslant 70$	23	
$70 < x \leqslant 80$	8	

(a) Copy and complete the table to show the mid-point values.

(b) Draw a frequency polygon to represent this data.

4 The frequency table shows the distances thrown in a school shot-put competition.

Distance, d (m)	Frequency	Mid-point value
$2.5 \leqslant d < 2.8$	4	
$2.8 \leqslant d < 3.1$	11	
$3.1 \leqslant d < 3.4$	8	
$3.4 \leqslant d < 3.7$	4	
$3.7 \leqslant d < 4.0$	3	

(a) Copy and complete the table, including the mid-point values.

(b) Draw a frequency polygon for this data.

Mixed Exercise

1 The table below shows the number of trees in each garden of houses along a particular section of the road.

House number	Number of trees	Pictogram
25	3	
27	5	
29	9	
31	4	
33	1	
35	6	

Copy and complete the table, using the symbol 🌳 to represent two trees.

2 The following table shows the typing speeds of 20 people (see question 2 of Exercise 11v).

Typing speed (words/min)	Frequency
31–40	1
41–50	8
51–60	9
61–70	2

Draw a bar chart to show this information.

3 The distribution of council tax in 2005 for a particular county council is shown in the following table:

Service	Amount (%)	Sector angle (°)
Borough council	15	
Police	10	
Fire	5	
County council	70	

(a) Copy and complete the table to include the sector angles.

(b) Draw a pie chart to show this information. Remember to include a key.

4 The table below shows the number of people waiting in a doctor's surgery during the morning session.

Time	Number of people
0900	4
0930	10
1000	8
1030	9
1100	6
1130	5
1200	2

(a) Draw a line graph for this data.

(b) When was the peak time for the surgery?

5 The table below shows the average distance travelled per litre
   of fuel by a range of engine sizes.

Engine size (cc)	1100	1400	1600	1800	2000	2200
km/ℓ	16.8	15.6	14.4	12.8	11.8	10.0

(a) Draw a scatter graph to show this information and show the best
    line of fit.

(b) What type of correlation is it?

6 Using the information in question 5 of Exercise 11ii, draw a frequency
   polygon for the data.

Checklist

You should know how to...	Grade	For more help, look back at Student Book pages...
draw pictograms, frequency diagrams and pie charts	G to D	295–308
draw time series line graphs and stem-and-leaf diagrams	E/D	308–312
construct scatter graphs and identify correlation	D/C	313–318
construct frequency polygons.	C	318–322

Exercise 12i

Links: 12A

> **What you should know**
>
> A ratio compares two or more quantities.

1 In a school the ratio of boys to girls is $4:3$.

    (a) If there are 16 boys in a class, how many girls are there?

    (b) If there are 90 girls in Year 10, how many people are there in Year 10 altogether?

Example:

Three boys to every two girls is written as the ratio of boys to girls as $3:2$.

2 A recipe for 16 ginger biscuits includes 240 g flour, 1 tsp ginger, 20 m*l* milk and 100 g treacle. How much of each ingredient would I need to make

    (a) 8 biscuits   **(b)** 32 biscuits   **(c)** 12 biscuits?

3 A model car is $\frac{1}{20}$ the size of the real thing.

    (a) What is the ratio of the model car to the real car?

    (b) If the height of the model is 9 cm, what is the height of the real car?

    (c) The car is 130 cm wide. What is the width of the model car?

4 Liquid plant food needs diluting with water in the ratio $2:25$. I have 170 m*l* of plant food, how much water should I add?

5 Purple paint is made by mixing red, blue and white paint in the ratio $3:5:2$. If I have 712 m*l* of blue paint, how much purple paint can I make?

Give your answer in litres.

Exercise 12ii

Links: 12B–D

> **What you should know**
>
> You can divide or multiply ratios to get them into their simplest form.
>
> When a ratio is in its simplest form you cannot divide the numbers any further.
>
> You can write a ratio as a fraction or in the form $1:n$ or $n:1$.

1 Write these ratios in their lowest terms.

    (a) $4:10$ **(b)** $15:6$ **(c)** $26:78$.

Example:

$160:120$

$16:12$ (dividing by 10)

$4:3$ (dividing by 4)

2 Write these ratios in their simplest forms.

Change quantities into the same units.

(a) £3.75:50p   (b) 400 m:2 km   (c) 60 g:3 kg

(d) 1.2:9.6   (e) $\frac{5}{6}:\frac{3}{4}$ (f) 1 m:50 cm:25 mm

3 In a box of apples, the number of good apples to rotten apples was 60:8.

(a) Write this ratio in its simplest form and then as a fraction.

(b) If I have 45 good apples in a box, how many rotten ones can I expect to find?

4 Write the following ratios in the form 1:n.

Change quantities into the same units first.

(a) 8 mm:3.6 cm   (b) 3 days:2 weeks   (c) 27p:£4.05

5 Write the following ratios in the form n:1.

Example:
10:3
1:3 ÷ 10
1:0.3

(a) 27:4   (b) 1 h:10 mins   (c) 1 year:5 months

Exercise 12iii

Links: 12E

> ## What you should know
>
> To divide a quantity in a given ratio:
>   1. work out the total number of parts
>   2. work out the value of one part
>   3. work out the value of each share.

1 Divide these amounts in the ratio given.

(a) 60 in the ratio of 5:1   (b) 48 in the ratio of 7:5

(c) 180 m*l* in the ratio of 4:5   (d) £7.50 in the ratio of 3:2

2 The ratio of boys to girls in a school is 6:7. If there are 221 pupils in Year 7, how many are girls?

3 Mandy and Simon receive money from their grandparents in the ratio of their ages. Mandy is 18 years old and Simon is 15 years old.

(a) Write the ratio of their ages in its simplest form.

(b) Their grandparents give them £115.50. How much will each receive?

5 A vet sees cats, dogs and birds in the ratio of 4:3:1. One day he sees 104 animals, how many of each type does he see?

6 Concrete for a path is made from cement, sand and gravel in the ratio of 2:4:3. If I need 1.53 t of concrete, how much of each ingredient do I need?

Exercise 12iv

Links: 12F

What you should know

Two quantities are in direct proportion if their ratio stays the same as they increase or decrease.

To solve problems involving direct proportion, find the cost of one unit first.

1   Work out the following by finding the cost of one first.

   (a) If seven ice creams cost £7.70, how much will three cost?

   (b) If 5 kg of potatoes cost £1.35, how much will 8 kg cost?

> **Example:**
> If three apples cost 45p, one apple costs
> 45 ÷ 3 = 15p and four apples cost 4 × 15p = 60p.

2   If 3.5 m of wood cost £4.34, how much would 2.6 m cost?

3   A café charges £1.75 for 400 ml of cola. How much would they charge for 750 ml?

4   Ali earns £41.20 for working eight hours.

   (a) How much does he earn per hour?

   (b) How much would he earn for working 15 hours?

   (c) One week he earned £61.80. How many hours had he worked?

5   I can travel 184 km on 5.2 l of petrol. How far could I travel on 12 l? Give your answer to the nearest kilometre.

6   Sally can jog 377 m in 58 s. If she continues to jog at the same speed, how far can she go in $1\frac{1}{2}$ mins?

Exercise 12v

Links: 12G

What you should know

Two quantities are in inverse proportion when one increases at the same rate that the other decreases.

1   It takes four plumbers five days to fit central heating in an office block. How long would it take ten plumbers?

2   A field can feed 20 sheep for ten days. If the farmer puts 25 sheep in the field, how long would it feed them for?

3   It takes a driver four hours to travel to London at a speed of 60 mph. In wintery conditions he can only manage an average speed of 40 mph. How long will it take him to get to London in winter?

> **Example:**
> Three people take six days to paint a house.
> One person takes
> 3 × 6 = 18 days.
> Nine people would take
> 18 ÷ 9 = 2 days.

4 It takes six pumps four days to pump out a flooded area.

  (a) How many pumps would be needed to complete the job in three days?

  (b) How many days would it take with only two pumps?

5 It takes $8\frac{1}{2}$ h to fly to Florida at a speed of 320 mph.

  (a) How long will it take at a speed of 400 mph? Give your answer in hours and minutes.

  (b) If it took 8 h 15 mins, what speed must I have been travelling? Give your answer to the nearest whole number.

Exercise 12vi

Links: 12I

> ## What you should know
>
> Map scales are written as ratios.

1 The scale of a map is 1 : 50 000. Find the distance on the ground that is represented by the following. Give your answers in sensible units.

  (a) 5 cm   **(b)** 15 cm   **(c)** 4.2 cm   **(d)** 7 mm

2 A map has a scale of 1 : 150 000. What measurement on the map represents the following. Give your answers to the nearest millimetre.

  (a) 6 km   **(b)** 10 km   **(c)** 9.75 km   **(d)** 69.3 km

3 A map of Australia has a scale of 1 : 10 000 000.

  (a) The distance from Canberra to Sydney is shown as 1.5 cm. What is the distance on the ground?

  (b) The distance from Sydney to Brisbane is 325 km. What measurement would this be on the map?

> A scale of 1 : 200 000 means that 1 cm on a map represents 200 000 cm on the ground. A sensible way of writing this would be as 2 km.

> Change the distances into cm before you divide.

Mixed Exercise

1 The ratio of motorcycles to scooters is 5 : 2. If there are 75 motorcycles, how many scooters are there?

2 A model train is made to a scale of 3 : 40.

  (a) The height of the model is 20 cm. How high is the real train?

  (b) The train is 7.4 m long. How long is the model?

3 The cost of making a bird box included labour at £5.50, wood at £1.20 and nails at 50p.

  (a) Write the ratio of labour to wood to nails in its simplest form.

  (b) I only have £14.40 worth of wood but plenty of nails. How many boxes can I make, and what would be the full cost?

4   At Barnaby Show, the ratio of cows to horses entered in competitions was $3:11$. If there were 378 animals, how many were cows?

5   The total cost of a holiday is £1428.50. This includes accommodation, travel and taxes in the ratio of $4:9:2$. What is the cost of each to the nearest penny?

6   I am paid £12.40 for delivering 1000 leaflets. What will I receive for delivering 720?

7   In Canada, four logging machines can cut down an area of forest in 15 days. How many machines will be needed to cut down the same area of forest in 12 days?

8   1.75 kg of fish cost £4.97.
   (a)   How much would 400 g of fish cost?
   (b)   If I paid 71p, how much fish would I get?

9   A map has a scale of $1:300\,000$.
   (a)   What does 3.8 cm on the map represent?
   (b)   What measurement on the map will represent 4.5 km?

Checklist

You should know about...	Grade	For more help, look back at Student Book pages...
using and simplifying ratios	F/E	326–330
ratios as fractions and in the form $1:n$	D/C	331–334
dividing in a ratio	D/C	334–336
direct proportion	E/D	336–338
inverse proportion	D/C	339–341
map scales.	E/D	342–344

Exercise 13i

Links: 13A

> **What you should know**
>
> The chance that something (an event) will happen is called probability.
>
> The probability of an event can be described using words such as certain, likely, even, unlikely and impossible.
>
> Probability also uses numbers to represent chance based on a probability scale between 0 and 1 ($0 \leqslant$ probability $\leqslant 1$).
>
> All probabilities are expressed as a fraction, decimal or as a percentage (0–100%).
>
> The probability that an event will happen is written as "P(event) = ".

1 What words would you use to describe the following events:

(a) The Moon is smaller than the Earth.

(b) Man will land on Mars within the next 20 years.

(c) Children will go into space.

(d) Man will land on the Sun.

(e) Life exists elsewhere in the Universe.

2 On the following probability scale, match the arrows to the following events that involve the throw of an octrahedral (eight-sided) dice.

(a) Throwing a 5.   **(b)** Obtaining a 9.

(c) Obtaining an even number.   **(d)** Throwing a number >3.

(e) Obtaining a prime number.

3 An ordinary six-sided dice is rolled. Write down, as a fraction, the probability that the number will be

(a) 4   **(b)** even   **(c)** prime   **(d)** <5.

4 A total of 220 raffle tickets were sold in aid of a local charity. If you buy five tickets, what is the probability of you winning first prize? Give your answer as a fraction in its lowest terms.

> Lowest terms is another way of saying *in its simplest form*.

5 A box of chocolates contains eight white (*w*), four dark (*d*) and six plain (*p*) chocolates.

(a) Write down the probabilities of the following events as fractions:

  (i) choosing a white chocolate

  (ii) choosing a white or plain chocolate

  (iii) choosing a white, dark or plain chocolate.

(b) Express the above results as decimals and percentages.

6 Each letter of the word PYTHAGORAS is written on a separate card. One card is chosen at random. Write down the probability that the card chosen will be

(a) the letter A   (b) the letter Y

(c) a vowel   (d) a consonant.

Exercise 13ii

Links: 13B

> **What you should know**
>
> relative frequency $= \dfrac{\text{number of successful trials}}{\text{total number of trials}}$
>
> frequency = total number of trials × relative frequency
>
> theoretical probability $= \dfrac{\text{number of successful outcomes}}{\text{total number of outcomes}}$

1 A ten-pence coin is tossed 100 times and the results recorded in a table.

	Frequency	Relative frequency	
		Decimal	Fraction
Head (H)	44		
Tail (T)	56		
Total	100		

Relative frequency is also called estimated or experimental probability.

(a) Copy and complete the table, giving the relative frequency as a fraction and as a decimal.

(b) Write down the theoretical probabilities P(H) and P(T).

(c) How do the results compare?

(d) How could the experimental results be improved?

2 An ordinary six-sided dice is rolled 500 times. Work out an estimate of how many times it will show

(a) a number 2   (b) an even number   (c) a number $\leqslant 4$.

3 A spinner is divided into five equal-sized sectors that contain the five vowels (as shown in the diagram). The spinner is spun 120 times and the results of the experiment recorded below.

Vowel	A	E	I	O	U
Frequency	19	28	22	17	34

   (a) Use the results to find the relative freqency for obtaining
      (i) the letter I   **(ii)** the letter O or U.

   (b) Work out the theoretical probability for these letters.

   (c) If the spiner is spun 1200 times, explain why the values shown in the table will not be 10-times larger.

4 Of 300 parsnip seeds sewn, only 255 germinate.

   (a) What is the relative frequency for germination, as a fraction in its lowest terms?

   (b) What is the relative frequency that the seeds will not germinate?

Exercise 13iii

Links: 13C

> **What you should know**
>
> If there are n mutually exclusive events that are all equally likely, the probability of each event happening is $\frac{1}{n}$.
>
> If there are n mutually exclusive events and m successful outcomes, the probability of a successful outcome is $\frac{m}{n}$.
>
> For any two events, say A and B, that are mutually exclusive and exhaustive, then P(A *or* B) = P(A) + P(B) = 1.
>
> For an event A, the probability of the event A *not* happening is P(*not* A) = 1 − P(A).

1 The probability that it will snow tomorrow is 0.3. What is the probability that it will not snow tomorrow?

2 The probability that a blue raffle ticket will be drawn from the tombola is $\frac{6}{75}$. What is the probability that the winning ticket will not be blue?

3 There are six blue, five red and four green paper clips in a box. What is the probability of picking out

   (a) a red paper clip   (b) *not* a blue paper clip?

4 The probability of a school netball team winning the next match is 0.30, and the probability of the team losing the next match is 0.55. Work out the probability of the team drawing the next match.

5 Fiona is going to a party and is unsure whether to wear the red, blue or black dress. The probability of her choosing the red dress is 0.45 and the probability of her choosing the blue dress is 0.15. What is the probability of Fiona wearing her black dress?

Exercise 13iv

Links: 13D

> **What you should know**
>
> Always list outcomes systematically.
> Outcomes should be shown as a list or in a sample space diagram, as appropriate.

1 Two spinners are spun together. They are shown here.

List all the possible outcomes.

Use your results to work out the probability of obtaining (blue, 3).

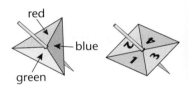

2 On a menu, there is a choice of two starters (soup or melon) and three main courses (pasta, lasagne or cannelloni). List all the possible outcomes.

3 John can play the guitar, piano and violin. Sarah can play the horn, trombone, recorder and flute.

(a) Copy and complete the sample space diagram.

		John		
		Guitar (g)	Piano (p)	Violin (v)
Sarah	Horn (h)			
	Trombone (t)		t, p	
	Recorder (r)			
	Flute (f)			

(b) How many musical combinations can the duo perform together?

4 Five-sided and three-sided spinners are spun together and their values added together to give a total.

(a) Construct a sample space diagram to show all the possible outcomes.

(b) What is the probability (as a fraction) that the total is

(i) more than 7   (ii) 0   (iii) less than 1?

Exercise 13v

Links: 13E

> ## What you should know
>
> Two events are independent if one outcome does not affect the other.
>
> For two independent events A and B:
>
> total number of outcomes $=$ number of outcomes of event A $\times$ number of outcomes of event B
>
> $P(A \ and \ B) = P(A) \times P(B)$.

1 A twenty-pence coin is tossed twice. What is the probability of obtaining two heads?

2 The twenty-pence coin in question 1 is tossed for a third time. Work out the probability of getting three heads.

3 An ordinary six-sided dice is rolled twice. What is the probability of obtaining a 3, followed by an even number?

4 There are three black and four white counters in a bag. Nicola selects a counter, notes its colour and returns it to the bag. She then picks another counter from the bag. What is the probability that Nicola picks

   (a) two black counters   **(b)** two white counters

   (c) one counter of each colour?

5 Two ordinary six-sided dice are rolled together, one is white and the other is red. Copy and complete a sample space diagram to show all of the likely outcomes.

		Red dice					
		1	2	3	4	5	6
White dice	1						
	2						
	3		(3, 2)				
	4					(4, 5)	
	5			(5, 3)			
	6						

What is the probability (as a fraction) of obtaining

  (a) the same numbers on both dice

  (b) an even number and an odd number

  (c) a total of 7

  (d) a difference of 2

  (e) the number on the red dice is smaller than the number on the white dice?

Mixed Exercise

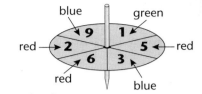

1 A coloured spinner has numbers 1, 2, 3, 5, 6 and 9.
   Write down the probability that, after one spin, the number
   obtained is

   (a) 2   **(b)** even   **(c)** odd   **(d)** 7

   (e) What is the probability of the spinner landing on a red number?

2 A fair, six-sided dice was thrown 100 times and the following results
   were recorded.

Number	1	2	3	4	5	6
Frequency	14	17	12	23	18	16

   (a) Write down the relative frequencies for each number.

   (b) What is the theoretical probability for each number?

   (c) How could the experimental results be improved?

3 Using the spinner in question 1, what is the probability that
   the spinner does *not* land on green?

4 There are five red, four blue and three yellow counters in a bag.
   What is the probability of

   (a) choosing a yellow counter   **(b)** *not* choosing a blue counter?

5 At an outdoor centre, there is a choice of two morning activities
   (abseiling or canoeing) and three afternoon activities (rock
   climbing, orienteering or a high-level rope course).

   (a) Construct a sample space diagram to show all the possible
   combinations of activities during the day.

   (b) What is the probability of *not* going climbing?

6 Damien uses the spinner in question 1. If he spins it twice,
   what is the probability that the spinner

   (a) lands on green twice

   (b) lands on red, followed by the number 5?

Checklist

You should know how to...	Grade	For more help, look back at Student Book pages...
write a probability and the values it can take	F to C	348–351
work out relative frequency and estimated probability	D/C	351–354
list outcomes and draw sample space diagrams	F to C	357–358
deal with mutually exclusive events and independent events.	F to D	354–357, 359–361

Exercise 14i

Links: 14A

> **What you should know**
>
> Even numbers divide exactly by 2, odd numbers do not.
> A prime number has only two factors: 1 and itself.
> A factor of a number is a number that divides into it exactly.
> A multiple is a number in its times table.

1 From this list of numbers, find the following sets of numbers:

9	8	3	6	17
4	15	12	1	21

   (a) odds   (b) prime numbers
   (c) any factors of 12 (d) multiples of 3

2 Write down the first five multiples of
   (a) 9   (b) 13   (c) 21

3 Find all the factors of
   (a) 18   (b) 24   (c) 49   (d) 50

   Make factor pairs.

4 Which of these numbers are
   (a) multiples of 9   (b) factors of 15

45	1	162	5
81	3	210	2

   (c) multiples of 6   (d) multiples of 6 and 9
   (e) factors of 15, 9 and 6?

Exercise 14ii

Links: 14B, 14C

> **What you should know**
>
> A square number is what you get when you multiply a whole number by itself.
> A cube number is what you get when you multiply a whole number by itself, then by itself again.
> The inverse of squaring is finding the square root. The inverse of cubing is finding the cube root.

1 Work out these squares and cubes.
   (a) 3^2 (b) 2^3 (c) 2.6^2 (d) 4.5^3 (e) 123^3

2 Which is larger?
   (a) 2^3 or 3^2 (b) 4^3 or 6^2 (c) 15^2 or 10^3

3 Work out the following:

(a) $3^2 + 4^2$ (b) $7^2 - 3^3$ (c) $5^2 + 9^2 - 4^3$

4 A square rug has sides of length 1.3 m. What is its area?

5 Work out

(a) $\sqrt{25}$ (b) $\sqrt{49}$ (c) $\sqrt[3]{8}$

(d) $\sqrt[3]{1000}$ (e) $\sqrt{64}$

6 Find the value of

(a) $\sqrt{50}$ (b) $\sqrt[3]{12}$ (c) $\sqrt{220}$

(d) $\sqrt[3]{100}$ (e) $\sqrt{4080}$

> Give your answer to 3 s.f.

7 Which is larger?

(a) $\sqrt{400}$ or 6^2 (b) $\sqrt{81}$ or 3^2

8 Work out

(a) $\sqrt[3]{3375} + 18^2$ (b) $\dfrac{\sqrt{3600} - 4^3}{2^2}$

Exercise 14iii

Links: 14D, 14E

> ### What you should know
>
> You can raise any number to a power.
>
> $x^n \times x^m = x^{n+m}$ $x^n \div x^m = x^{n-m}$ $x^{-n} = \dfrac{1}{x^n}$

1 Write the following using index notation.

(a) $4 \times 4 \times 4 \times 4 \times 4$

(b) $10 \times 10 \times 10 \times 10 \times 10 \times 10 \times 10$

2 Work out the value of

(a) 2^8 (b) 6^4 (c) 15^5 (d) 2^{12} (e) $(2.3)^4$

3 Find the value of x in the following.

(a) $2^x = 128$ (b) $3^x = 243$ (c) $10^x = 1\,000\,000$

4 Write each of these as a single power.

(a) $5^3 \times 5^6$ (b) $4^2 \times 4^3$ (c) $7^3 \times 7^2 \times 7^3$

> *Example:*
>
> $2^3 \times 2^4 = 2^{(3+4)} = 2^7$

5 Write each of these as a single power.

(a) $7^6 \div 7^3$ (b) $\dfrac{10^5}{10^3}$ (c) $5^2 \div 5^2$

> *Example:*
>
> $3^6 \div 3^4 = 3^{(6-4)} = 3^2$

6 Give a reason why you are unable to write the following as a single power.

(a) $3^2 + 3^4$ (b) $4^2 \times 5^3$ (c) $9^5 - 9^3$

7 Simplify the following by writing each one as a single power.

(a) $10^3 \times 10^6 \div 10^4$ (b) $\dfrac{4^5}{4^2 \times 4^2}$

(c) $\dfrac{(5^4 \times 5^6)}{(5^2 \times 5^4)}$ (d) $\dfrac{(9^2 \times 9^3 \times 9^5)}{(9^4 \times 9^2)}$

8 Work out the value of your answers to question 7.

Exercise 14iv   **Links: 14F**

What you should know

To write a number as a product of its prime factors, you can split the number down using factor trees or you divide by the smallest prime number each time.

1 Write these numbers as the product of their prime factors.
Give your answers in index form.

(a) 12 (b) 18 (c) 50 (d) 100
(e) 75 (f) 48 (g) 120 (h) 144

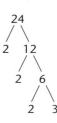

2 Give a reason for your answer to each of the following.

(a) Is 13 a prime factor of 273?

(b) Is 19 a prime factor of 286?

3 (a) List the prime factors of 45.

(b) List the prime factors of 60.

(c) Which prime factors are common to both 45 and 60?

Exercise 14v   **Links: 14G, 14H**

What you should know

To find the highest common factor (HCF), write each number as a product of prime factors and then multiply the prime factors common to both numbers.

To find the lowest common multiple (LCM), write each number as a product of prime factors and then multiply the prime factors in both lists without duplication.

1 (a) List the prime factors of 12 and 18.

(b) Find the HCF of 12 and 18.

2 Find the HCF of

  (a) 30 and 50   **(b)** 20 and 32   **(c)** 75 and 120

3 Find the HCF of the following:

  (a) 12, 16 and 20   **(b)** 27, 36 and 45

4 **(a)** List the first eight multiples of the number 6.

  (b) List the first five multiples of number 9.

  (c) List all the multiples that are common to the numbers 6 and 9.

  (d) What is the LCM of the numbers 6 and 9?

5 Find the LCM of

  (a) 4 and 6   **(b)** 18 and 15   **(c)** 12 and 16

6 Find the LCM of

  (a) 15, 20 and 30   **(b)** 12 16 and 24

7 On Sunday morning the church bell rings every 10 mins and the church clock chimes every 15 mins. Mr Jones only wakes up when they both go off together. How long does he sleep after they first start?

> **Example:**
> Prime factors of 28 are
> **2** × 2 × **7**
> Prime factors of 42 are
> **2** × 3 × **7**
> HCF = **2** × **7** = 14
> LCM = 2 × 2 × 3 × 7 = 84

Mixed Exercise

1 Using these numbers, write down any numbers that are

  (a) prime   **(b)** factors of 20   **(c)** multiples of 4   **(d)** even

> 12, 2, 5, 1, 16, 20, 40, 9

2 Work out

  (a) 9^2 **(b)** 3^3 **(c)** $\sqrt{49}$ **(d)** $\sqrt[3]{8}$ **(e)** 2^7

3 Write as a single power

  (a) $7^3 \times 7^2$ **(b)** $6^5 \div 6^3$ **(c)** $\dfrac{2^3 \times 2^5}{2^4 \times 2}$ **(d)** $\dfrac{3^9 \times 3^2}{3^3}$

4 Find the prime factors of 18 and 30. Use them to find the HCF and LCM of 18 and 30.

Checklist

You should know about...	Grade	For more help, look back at Student Book pages...
multiples, factors and prime numbers	G to E	366–369
square, cube, square root and cube root numbers	G to E	369–374
laws of indices and calculating powers	C	374–377
prime factors, HCF and LCM.	C	377–383

15 Percentages and money

Exercise 15i

Links: 15A

> **What you should know**
>
> To find a percentage of a quantity, write the percentage as a fraction or decimal and multiply by the quantity.

1 Work out

    (a) 1% of £350   **(b)** 10% of 67 km   **(c)** 5% of 48 kg

2 Find

    (a) 18% of 550 g   **(b)** 64% of 3840 km   **(c)** 27% of 98 m*l*

> *Example:*
> Find 15% of 250 g.
> $\frac{15}{100} \times 250 = 37.5\,g$
> or $0.15 \times 250 = 37.5\,g$

3 Paul got 72% in his maths test and 68% in his English test. If both tests were out of 75, how many marks did he get for each subject?

4 House prices have risen by 13% this year. I paid £125 000 for my house a year ago, how much is it worth now?

5 A slimmers meal read "only 4% fat". If the mass of the meal was 425 g, how many grams of fat did it contain?

6 A recent survey showed that 68% of households have at least one car. There are 12 840 households in Barton. How many do *not* have a car?

Exercise 15ii

Links: 15B

> **What you should know**
>
> To increase or decrease a quantity by a given percentage:
>
> Method A: work out the percentage and then either add it on or take it off the amount.
>
> Method B: add or subtract the percentage from 100 and then find this new percentage of the amount.

1 *Increase* the following by the percentage given.

    (a) £200 by 15%   **(b)** 48 m by 36%   **(c)** 7250 by 46%

2 *Decrease* the following by the percentage given.

    (a) 700 kg by 8%   **(b)** 3200 by 12%   **(c)** 86 m*l* by 63%

3 Sally was given a 4% pay rise. She earned £6.50 per hour before the pay rise. How much will she earn per hour now?

4 A bed was priced at £120. In a sale, it was reduced by 15%. How much will the bed cost now?

5 The number of seals spotted in the river Tees this year has increased by 8%. If there were 75 seen last year, how many were seen this year?

6 The population of finches is counted twice a year. It was found the number increases by 28% in April when the eggs hatched but then decreases by 15% in September. In one area it was estimated that there was a population of 3000 finches in March. How many were there at the end of **(a)** April **(b)** September?

▦ Exercise 15iii

Links: 15C

> **What you should know**
>
> To write one quantity as a percentage of another, first write the two quantities as a fraction, then multiply by 100 to convert to a percentage.

1 Work out

(a) 5 as a percentage of 20

(b) 62 as a percentage of 80

Example:

7 as a percentage of 10 is the same as $\frac{7}{10}$.

$\frac{7}{10} \times 100 = 70\%$

Give all your answers to 2 d.p.

2 In her end of year exams, Alice scored the following marks. Write these as percentages. Is she better at science or history?

Subject	English	Maths	Geography	History	Science
Score	$\frac{63}{80}$	$\frac{75}{90}$	$\frac{34}{50}$	$\frac{42}{60}$	$\frac{52}{75}$

3 The school youth club has 225 members. There are 84 students from Year 11 in the club, what percentage is this?

4 At football practice, Ali scored in 13 out of 22 attempts at goal. Jason scored in 7 out of 18 attempts. Who was better at scoring?

Change them both into percentages to compare them.

▦ Exercise 15iv

Links: 15D, 15E

> **What you should know**
>
> percentage change $= \dfrac{\text{actual amount}}{\text{original amount}} \times 100$
>
> percentage profit (or loss) $= \dfrac{\text{actual profit (or loss)}}{\text{cost price}} \times 100$

1 In a sale, a DVD recorder was reduced from £98 to £64. What is the percentage reduction?

Give your answer to 1 d.p.

2 The number of deer in a glen in Scotland has increased from 484 last year to 515 this year. What is the percentage increase?

3 The number of students in each year group has changed throughout the year. What is the percentage change for each year group? Give your answers to one decimal place.

Year	7	8	9	10	11
September	212	206	208	198	192
July	224	172	212	188	190

4 Tom had a pay increase from £146 per week to £152.50. What was the percentage increase in pay? Give your answer to two decimal places.

5 Molly bought a bag for £4 at a car boot sale. She sold it for £5.

    (a) How much profit did she make?

    (b) What was the percentage profit?

6 Scott bought a DVD for £12.99. He sold it for £3.50.

    (a) How much money did he lose?

    (b) What was the percentage loss to the nearest 1%?

7 A house was sold for £178 000. It had originally cost the owner £140 000. What was the percentage profit?

8 A business man bought footballs in bulk. 500 footballs cost him £1750. He sold them for £5.50 each.

    (a) How much profit did he make?

    (b) What was his percentage profit?

Exercise 15v

Links: 15F, 15G

> ## What you should know
>
> To work out the total cost with value-added tax (VAT), work out $17\frac{1}{2}\%$ and add it on, or find $117\frac{1}{2}\%$ of the cost.
>
> The full cost of buying on credit includes paying a deposit plus a number of regular payments.

1 Work out the total cost of

    (a) a DVD at £17 + VAT   **(b)** a TV at £145 + VAT.

> Take VAT to be $17\frac{1}{2}\%$ throughout this exercise.
> Give all your answers to the nearest penny.

2 Libby buys a scooter. It costs £175 plus VAT. How much is the total cost of the scooter?

3 The gas bill for one-quarter of a year is £84.50 plus VAT. What is the total cost of the bill?

4 **(a)** What is the total cost of buying a bike priced at £98 if you pay an 8% deposit and make 12 monthly payments of £9?

    (b) How much more do you pay on credit?

5   A carpet costs £148. Alex decides to pay for it on credit. He pays
    a 5% deposit, followed by 18 monthly payments of £12.50. How
    much more does it cost to buy it on credit?

Exercise 15vi

Links: 15H

> ### What you should know
>
> basic pay = number of hours × rate of pay
> Overtime is often paid at a different rate.

1   How much will I earn for a 15-hour week if my hourly pay is
    (a) £5.20   (b) £5.65   (c) £6.50?

2   I am paid £6.60 per hour, how much will I get for overtime at
    (a) double-time   (b) time-and-a-half?

> Time-and-a-half rate = hourly
> rate + ½ of hourly rate.
> Give all your answers to the
> nearest penny.

3   Callum is paid £5.84 per hour. He works a 38-hour week and is
    then paid time-and-a-half for overtime. One week, he works 45
    hours. How much does he earn?

4   Mr Robinson works 35 h/week for which he is paid £8.70 per
    hour. On Saturdays, he works 6-hours' overtime at a rate of
    time-and-a-half and on Sundays, he works 4-hours' overtime at
    double-time. What does he earn each week?

5   David is paid £10.20 per hour no matter how long he works. One
    week he earned £397.80. How many hours did he work?

6   Sarah is paid £6.28 per hour for a 40-hour week and time-and-a-
    quarter for overtime.
    (a) Sarah works 47 hours. How much will she earn?
    (b) One week Sarah earns £274.75. How many hours overtime
         does she work?

Exercise 15vii

Links: 15I, 15J

> ### What you should know
>
> To work out the best buy, work out how much it costs for 1 unit (the smallest cost is best),
> or how much you get for 1p (the biggest answer is best).
>
> Bills for household services are sometimes made up of two parts, a standing charge and the
> cost of the units of gas (or electricity) used.

1   I can buy a 200 g box of sweets for £1.00 or a 50 g packet for
    20p. Which one is the best buy?

> Work out how many grams
> you get for 1p.

2 A box containing 50 apples costs £4.50 and a box of 70 apples costs £7.14. Which is the best buy?

3 Tom and Mel have identical cars, but they use different types of petrol. Unleaded petrol takes Tom 160 miles on 14 *l*. Four-star petrol takes Mel 190 miles on 23 *l*. If both types of petrol cost the same per litre, which one would be the best buy?

> Work out how far you can go on 1 ℓ of petrol.

4 Jane's mum uses 520 units of electricity. The company charges 100 units at 9.5p/unit and the remainder at 7.6p/unit.

   (a) How much will she have to pay for the first 100 units?

   (b) How much will she have to pay altogether?

> Work out how many units are left to pay for at 7.6p.

5 Work out the gas bills for the following houses. There is a standing charge of £12.40 for each house.

House no.	Previous reading	Present reading	Unit price for first 100	Unit price for remainder
21	12453	13248	7.3p	4.2p
22	61428	69572	6.4p	5.1p
23	47529	58642	4.2p	2.9p

Exercise 15viii

Links: 15K

> ### What you should know
>
> Simple interest is where the interest is the same each year.
>
> $$\text{simple interest} = \frac{P \times R \times T}{100}, \quad \text{time} = \frac{100 \times I}{P \times R}, \quad \text{rate} = \frac{100 \times I}{P \times T}, \quad \text{principal} = \frac{100 \times I}{R \times T}$$

1 Work out the simple interest earned on £300 invested for three years at a rate of 4% per year.

> The amount invested is the *principal*.

2 Work out the number of years I will have to invest £400 at a rate of 5% simple interest to earn £60 interest.

3 James invests £150 for four years at a rate of 6% per year (simple interest). How much in total will he have at the end of four years?

Mixed Exercise

1 Ranjit earns £15 000 per year. He has 22% deducted from his pay for income tax and national insurance. How much

   (a) is deducted from his pay   **(b)** does he take home?

2 24% of pupils in a school are left-handed. If there are 1025 pupils in the school, how many are right-handed?

3 John's car depreciated by 23% in one year. If he bought it for £6400 last year, how much is it worth now?

4 Jason earns £18 000. He said that when his pay increases by 4% in June and then again by 4% in July, it will be the same as his pay increasing by 8%. Is he correct?

5 What is 8 as a percentage of 40?

6 A car cost £4200. After one year, it was valued at £3600. What is the percentage reduction in value?

7 A gardener buys a packet of 24 tomato seeds for £1.15. He plants them in pots and when they are big enough he sells them at 75p each. If the pots and compost cost him £5.10, what is his percentage profit?

8 Reni's hotel bill is £48 plus VAT. What will be the total cost of the bill if the VAT rate is $17\frac{1}{2}$%?

9 A home cinema system cost £625. Four flatmates decide to pay for it on credit. They have to pay 12% deposit followed by 12 monthly payments of £62. How much will each one have to pay?

10 Mr Robinson works 35 h/week for which he is paid £9.40 per hour. On Saturdays, he works 7-hours' overtime at time-and-a-half. How much does he earn?

11 A bottle of antiseptic costs £3 for 30 m*l* or £2.75 for 25 m*l*. Which one is the best buy?

12 A gas company charges 5.3p for the first 150 units used and then 2.6p for the remaining units used. They also have a standing charge of £7.50. If I use 762 units of gas, how much will I have to pay?

13 I invested £750 for two years at a rate of 6% simple interest. How much will I have at the end of the two years?

Checklist

You should know how to...	Grade	For more help, look back at Student Book pages...
find a percentage of a quantity	G to E	387–389
find percentages, increases and decreases	D	389–392
write one quantity as a percentage of another	E/D	392–393
calculate percentage change and profit and loss	C	393–397
work out VAT, credit and wages	E/D	397–403
understand best buys and bills	G to D	403–407
calculate simple interest.	E to C	407–412

Exercise 16i

Links: 16A, 16B

> **What you should know**
>
> To write the next term in a sequence it helps to look at the differences between consecutive terms.

1 Here is a number sequence.

   5, 9, 13, 17, 21, ...

   (a) Write down the second term.

   (b) Write down the fifth term.

   (c) Describe the rule for continuing the sequence.

   (d) Write down the next three terms.

2 For each sequence

   (i) describe the rule for continuing the sequence

   (ii) write down the fifth and sixth terms.

   (a) 7, 10, 13, 16, ...   **(b)** 2, 8, 14, 20, ...

   (c) 5, 14, 23, 32, ...   **(d)** 8, 15, 22, 29, ...

   (e) −5, −1, 3, 7, ...   **(f)** −6, −3, 0, 3, ...

3 Here is a number sequence.

   26, 22, 18, 14, ...

   (a) Write down the second term.

   (b) Write down the fourth term.

   (c) Describe the rule for continuing the sequence.

   (d) Write down the next three terms.

4 For each sequence that follows

   (i) describe the rule for continuing the sequence

   (ii) write down the fifth and sixth terms.

   (a) 48, 42, 36, 30, ...   **(b)** 44, 39, 34, 29, ...

   (c) 77, 69, 61, 53, ...   **(d)** 65, 56, 47, 38, ...

   (e) 17, 13, 9, 5, ...   **(f)** 20, 14, 8, 2, ...

5 Here is a number sequence.

5, 7, 10, 14, 19, ...

(a) Find the differences between consecutive terms.

(b) Describe the pattern of the differences.

(c) Write down the next three terms.

6 For each sequence, find the next three terms.

(a) 7, 8, 10, 13, ...

(b) 3, 5, 9, 15, ...

(c) 5, 6, 9, 14, ...

(d) 4, 9, 19, 34, ...

(e) −5, −1, 4, 10, ...

(f) 1, 2, 4, 8, 16, ...

(g) 49, 38, 28, 19, ...

(h) 20, 15, 11, 8, ...

Use differencees to help you.

Exercise 16ii

Links: 16C

What you should know

The general term or nth term is a general rule to work out any term in a sequence if you know its position.

1 The general rule of a sequence is 2 × the term number and then add 3.

(a) Use the rule to find the first three terms.

(b) Use the rule to write down the 15th term.

2 The general rule of a sequence is 4 × the term number and then subtract 2.

(a) Use the rule to find the first three terms.

(b) Use the rule to write down the 50th term.

3 For each of the following sequences

(i) write down the first four terms

(ii) find the difference between consecutive terms

(iii) write down the 20th term.

(a) nth term: $2n + 1$

(b) nth term: $3n − 2$

(c) nth term: $5n + 3$

(d) nth term: $4n + 7$

(e) nth term: $6n − 4$

(f) nth term: $2n − 5$

4 The nth term of a sequence is $5n + 2$.

(a) Work out the value of the fourth term.

(b) Which term has a value of 47?

(c) Explain why 73 is not a term in this sequence.

5 The nth term of a sequence is $n^2 + 2$.

(a) Write down the first four terms.

(b) Write down the 12th term.

(c) Explain why 36 is not a term in this sequence.

Exercise 16iii

Links: 16D

What you should know

If the difference between consecutive terms is the same you can use it to find the rule for the *n*th term.

Find the *n*th term and the 30th term of each of these sequences.

1 4, 6, 8, 10, ...

2 7, 10, 13, 16, ...

3 2, 7, 12, 17, ...

4 6, 10, 14, 18, ...

5 5, 11, 17, 23, ...

6 0, 4, 8, 12, ...

7 11, 18, 25, 32, ...

8 −1, 1, 3, 5, ...

9 −5, −2, 1, 4, ...

10 17, 15, 13, 11, ...

> If the difference is 3, then the *n*th term includes 3*n*. Then compare the terms of the sequence with the numbers in the 3× table.

Exercise 16iv

Links: 16E

What you should know

Sequences of diagrams can lead to number squences.

1 Matchsticks are used to make patterns of hexagons.

 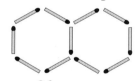 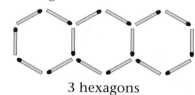

1 hexagon   2 hexagons   3 hexagons

(a) Draw the pattern for four hexagons.

(b) How many matchsticks are needed for five hexagons?

(c) Describe the rule for continuing the sequence of the number of matchsticks needed.

(d) How many matchsticks are needed for 12 hexagons?

(e) How many matchsticks are needed for *n* hexagons?

(f) How many hexagons can you make with 101 matchsticks?

2 Black and white square tiles are used to make patterns.

 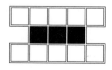 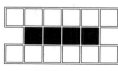

Pattern 1   Pattern 2   Pattern 3

(a) Draw pattern 4.

(b) How many of each colour tile are needed for pattern 5?

(c) Describe the rule for continuing the sequence of the number of black tiles needed.

(d) How many black tiles are needed for pattern n?

(e) How many white tiles are needed for pattern n?

Mixed Exercise

1 For each sequence

  (i) describe the rule for continuing the sequence

  (ii) write down the fifth and sixth terms.

  (a) 12, 17, 22, 27, ...   (b) 4, 10, 16, 22, ...

  (c) 8, 11, 14, 17, ...   (d) 55, 45, 35, 25, ...

  (e) 21, 19, 17, 15, ...   (f) 34, 27, 20, 13, ...

2 For each sequence, find the next three terms.

  (a) 10, 11, 13, 16, ...   (b) 2, 3, 6, 11, ...

  (c) 7, 9, 13, 19, ...   (d) 4, 9, 15, 22, ...

  (e) −3, 1, 7, 15, ...   (f) 51, 43, 36, 30, ...

3 For each of the following sequences, write down the first four terms.

  (a) nth term: $2n + 5$ (b) nth term: $4n − 1$

  (c) nth term: $5n − 4$ (d) nth term: $6n + 3$

  (e) nth term: $4n − 5$ (f) nth term: $n^2 + 6$

4 Find the nth term and the 20th term of each of these sequences.

  (a) 12, 17, 22, 27, ...   (b) 4, 10, 16, 22, ...

  (c) 8, 12, 16, 20, ...   (d) 8, 10, 12, 14, ...

  (e) 4, 5, 6, 7, ...   (f) 13, 11, 9, 7, ...

Checklist

You should know how to ...	Grade	For more help, look back at Student Book pages...
continue sequences of numbers	G to E	419–421
find differences	G to E	421–422
use the general term of a sequence	D	423–426
find the nth term of a sequence	C	426–4237
find sequences of diagrams.	G to C	427–432

Exercise 17i

Links: 17A

> **What you should know**
>
> When using compasses you must leave the construction arcs as evidence that you have used the correct method

Construct triangles with these measurements.

> It helps to draw and label a sketch first.

1 $AB = 10$ cm $AC = 7$ cm $BC = 8.5$ cm

2 $AB = 9$ cm $AC = 6$ cm $BC = 5$ cm

3 $AB = 7.5$ cm $AC = 10$ cm $BC = 6$ cm

> Constructions must be drawn using only a straight edge (ruler) and pair of compasses.

4 An equilateral triangle of side 8 cm.

5 An isosceles triangle of sides 9 cm, 9 cm and 4 cm.

Exercise 17ii

Links: 17C–F

> **What you should know**
>
> A perpendicular bisector cuts a line segment in half, and is perpendicular to the line segment.
> The bisector of an angle divides an angle into two equal parts.

1 **(a)** Construct
  (i) the angle bisector of angle A
  (ii) the perpendicular from C to the line AB.

(b) If **(i)** and **(ii)** meet at point P, measure AP.

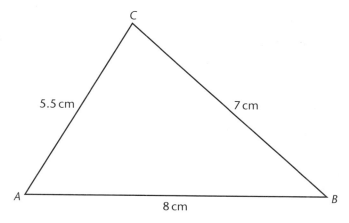

2 Make an accurate copy of triangle *PQR*.

    (a) Start by drawing *PQ* = 5 cm.

    (b) Construct an angle of 60° at *P*.

    (c) Construct an angle of 90° at *Q*.

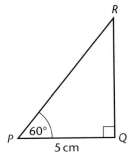

3 Make an accurate copy of triangle *FGH*.

    (a) Start by drawing *FG* = 6 cm.

    (b) Construct an angle of 90° at *F*.

    (c) Construct the angle bisector of your 90° angle (giving an angle of 45°).

    (d) Join *H* to *G* and measure the length of *HG*.

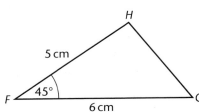

4 Make an accurate copy of this quadrilateral.

    (a) Start by drawing *LM* = 10 cm.

    (b) From *M*, construct an angle of 90°, measure 9 cm along it to find point *N*.

    (c) From *N*, construct an angle of 60°, measure 8 cm along it to find point *P*.

    (d) Join *P* to *L* and measure the length of *PL*.

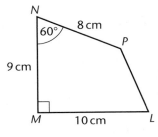

5 (a) Construct the perpendicular bisectors of all three sides (they should meet in a point, call it *X*).

    (b) Put your compass point on *X* and using *X* as centre, draw a circle which passes through points *D*, *E* and *F* (this is called the CIRCUMCIRCLE of the triangle).

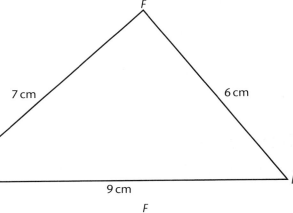

6 (a) Construct the angle bisectors of all three angles of the triangle (they should meet in a point, call it *Y*).

    (b) Put your compass point on *Y* and using *Y* as the centre, draw a circle which lies inside the triangle but just touches each of the sides *DE*, *DF* and *EF* (this is called the INCIRCLE of the triangle).

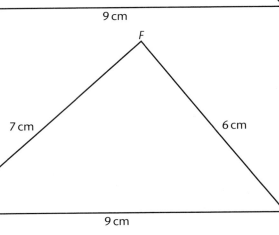

Exercise 17iii

Links: 17G

> ## What you should know
>
> A locus is a set of points that obey a given rule.
>
> For locus questions, think about the points, make a sketch and construct the locus using standard constructions.

Use accurate constructions to answer these questions.

1 **(a)** Construct a triangle *ABC* where *AB* = 8 cm, *AC* = 6 cm and *BC* = 5 cm.

    (b) Shade the region where points are

        (i) more than 5 cm from *A*

        (ii) nearer to *C* than *B*.

2 **(a)** Construct a triangle *LMN* where *LM* = 10 cm, *LN* = 7.5 cm and *MN* = 5.5 cm.

    (b) Shade the region where points are

        (i) nearer to *L* than *M*

        (ii) closer to *MN* than *LM*.

3 **(a)** Construct a triangle *PQR* where *PQ* = 9 cm, *PR* = 6.5 cm and *QR* = 7.5 cm.

    (b) Shade the region where points are

        (i) nearer to *P* than *Q*

        (ii) closer to *PQ* than *PR*

        (iii) less than 4 cm from *R*.

Exercise 17iv

Links: 17H

1 Two aircraft *A* and *B* are shown in the diagram.

A•

> Use a scale of 1 cm for 500 metres.

B •

Aircraft *A* flies on a bearing of 230°.
Copy the diagram and mark clearly all points where aircraft *A* is within 2000 metres of aircraft *B*.

2 The diagram shows two cars, *A* and *B*, and a speed detector van, *D*.

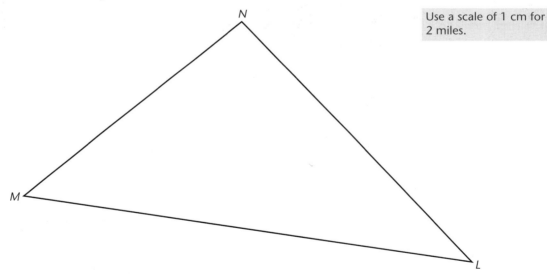

Car *A* is travelling on the M4 on a bearing of 065°.
Car *B* is travelling on the M5 on a bearing of 035°.
The speed of the cars can be monitored when they are within 600 metres of the detector van.
Work out the distance for which each car is within the range of the detector van.

Use a scale of 1 cm for 200 metres.

3 The diagram shows three towns *L*, *M* and *N*, connected by main roads.
LM = 24 miles, *LN* = 18 miles and *MN* = 15 miles.

Use a scale of 1 cm for 2 miles.

An out of town business park is to be built inside triangle *LMN* so that it is,

(a) nearer to *N* than *M*,

(b) at least 3 miles from any of the main roads, *LM*, *LN* and *MN*.

(c) at least 12 miles from *L*.

Copy the diagram and shade the region where the business park can be built.

4 Quadrilateral *PQRS* is such that *PQ* = 7 cm, *QR* = 4 cm, *RS* = 6 cm and *PS* = 5 cm.

Copy the diagram and shade the region that satisfies all of these conditions.

(a) closer to *PQ* than *PS*

(b) nearer to *R* than *S*

(c) less than 3.5 cm from *R*

(d) more than 2 cm from *QR*.

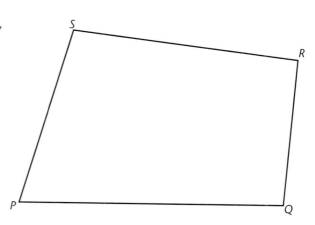

Mixed exercise

1 Construct a triangle with measurements *AB* = 13 cm, *AC* = 5 cm, *BC* = 12 cm.

2 (a) Construct a triangle *XYZ* where *XY* = 7 cm, *XZ* = 8.5 cm and *YZ* = 8.5 cm.

(b) Shade the region where points are

(i) nearer to *Y* than *X*

(ii) closer to *YZ* than *YX*

(iii) at least 4.5 cm from *Z*

3 *ABC* is a triangular area of sea where *AB* = 90 miles, *AC* = 80 miles and *BC* = 100 miles.
Treasure lies at the bottom of the sea and is

(a) between bearings of 050° and 080° from *A*,

(b) closer to *CB* than *CA*,

(c) nearer to *B* than *C*,

(d) more than 50 miles from *B*.

Use a scale of 1 cm for 10 miles and make accurate constructions to find the region where the treasure lies. Shade the region.

Checklist

You should know how to...	Grade	For more help, look back at Student Book pages...
construct a triangle given all three sides	E	436–437
construct perpendiculars	C	438–441
construct angles	C	441–444
construct loci	C	444–449
construct loci using bearings and scale drawings	E/D	449–451

Exercise 18i

Links: 18A

> **What you should know**
>
> Coordinates are always given as (x, y). The grid is called the x–y coordinate grid.
> Positive and negative x and y values give four areas or quadrants within the coordinate grid.
> A straight line that joins two points $A(x_1, y_1)$ and $B(x_2, y_2)$ on a coordinate grid is called a line segment. The mid-point of a line segment is given by the coordinate
> $$\left(\frac{x_1 + x_2}{2}, \frac{y_1 + y_2}{2}\right).$$

1 The coordinate grid shows eight points (A–H).
   Write down the coordinates of each point in the
   form (x, y).

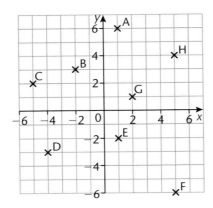

2 (a) On squared paper, draw the coordinate grid with axes
       between -6 and 6.

   (b) Plot the following points and join them up in the order
       given.

   $E(4, 5), F(6, -3), G(-5, -3), H(-1, 5)$

   (c) What is the name of the shape you have drawn?

   (d) Describe the lines that join H to E and G to F?

3 Look at the following diagram.

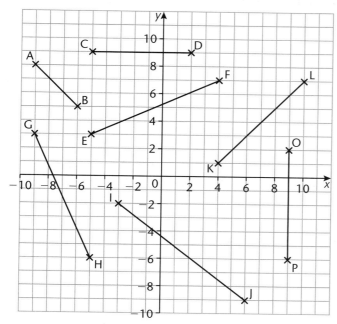

For each line segment, write down the coordinates of both end points and work out the coordinates of the mid-point of each of the lines.

4 Without drawing the lines, work out the coordinates of the mid-points of each of the following line segments.

(a) PQ, with P(6, 4) and Q(3, 2)

(b) RS, with R(20, 18) and S(10, 9)

(c) TU, with T(8, 2) and U(12, 6)

(d) VW, with V(−6, 8) and W(4, −6)

(e) XY, with X(−1, −8) and Y(−2, 4)

Exercise 18ii

Links: 18B

What you should know

In a straight-line graph, there is a linear relationship between x and y. The equation is called a linear equation and the graph is called a linear graph.

A line that is parallel to the x-axis has an equation $x = a$, where a is a number.

A line that is parallel to the y-axis has an equation $y = b$, where b is a number.

1 From the graph shown at the top of the next page, write down the equations of the lines that are

(a) parallel to the x-axis   (b) parallel to the y-axis.

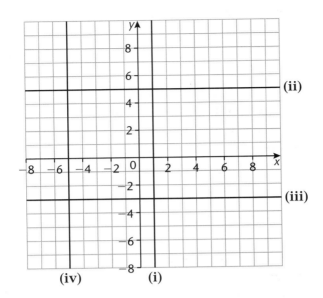

2 Draw a coordinate grid with both the x-axis and the y-axis
   with values between -6 and 6. On your grid, draw the lines

   (a) $x = 3$ (b) $x = 6$ (c) $x = -5$

   (d) $y = 5$ (e) $y = -1$ (f) $y = -4$

3 What are the equations of the lines that represent

   (a) the x-axis   (b) the y-axis?

Exercise 18iii

Links: 18C

> ## What you should know
>
> For lines that are not parallel to either the x-axis or the y-axis, construct a table with a minimum of three points. Plot all three points and draw a straight line within the range of x-values given.

1 (a) Copy and complete the following table.

x	-6	0	6
$y = x$			
$y = x + 2$			
$y = x - 4$			

   (b) For each linear equation, plot the three points and draw
        the graph on the same x–y coordinate grid, with x-axis
        values between -6 and 6 and y-axis values between -10
        and 10.

2 (a) Construct a table of results for each linear equation, using the range of x values shown.

   (i) $y = x$, using x values of 0, 3 and 6

   (ii) $y = 2x$, using x values of 0, 2 and 3

   (iii) $y = 3x$, using x values of 0, 1 and 2

   (b) Draw a coordinate grid with x and y values between 0 and 6. Plot these points and draw the straight lines.

   (c) What do you notice about the three lines you have drawn?

   (d) What effect does increasing the value of the number in front of the x have?

3 (a) Construct the appropriate table of results for the following linear equations.

   (i) $y = 2x + 2$ (ii) $y = 2x - 4$ (iii) $y = 2x + \frac{1}{2}$

   (b) Draw the three lines on the same coordinate grid.

   (c) What do you notice about the three lines you have drawn?

Exercise 18iv

Links: 18D

What you should know

$$\text{gradient} = \frac{\text{vertical distance}}{\text{horizontal distance}}$$

The gradient is the same as the number in front of the x in the equation of the line.

Straight lines that are parallel have identical gradients.

Sometimes it is necessary to alter the linear equation to make y the subject.

1 Write down the gradient of the lines in question 2 of Exercise 18iii.

2 Look at the following equations of straight lines. In each case, write down the gradient of the line.

   (a) $y = 4x - 1$ (b) $y = 2x + 7$ (c) $y = 20x - 10$

   (d) $y = -3x + 4$ (e) $y = 5 - 2x$ (f) $y = -7x$

3 Alter the following equations to make y the subject. In each case, write down the gradient of the line.

   (a) $y + 3 = 5x$ (b) $3x + y = 8$ (c) $y - 4x = 9$

   (d) $4x = y - 6$ (e) $-2x = 4 - y$ (f) $y - x - 1 = 0$

4 Without plotting these straight lines, identify all the lines that are parallel to the line $y = 2x - 3$.

   (a) $y = 3x - 2$ (b) $y = 4x - 6$ (c) $y = -3 + 2x$

   (d) $y + 2 = 3x$ (e) $3 = 2x - y$ (f) $2y = 4x - 6$

Exercise 18v

Links: 18E

> ### What you should know
>
> The point where a line crosses the y-axis is called the y-intercept. The y-intercept is simply a number.

1 Write down the value of the y-intercepts for the lines in question 2 of Exercise 18iv.

2 Write down the value of the y-intercepts for the lines in question 3 of Exercise 18iv.

3 For the following linear equations, identify the equations that have the same y-intercept value as the equation $y = 3x - 2$.

    (a) $y = 4x - 2$ **(b)** $y - 2 = 3x$

    (c) $3x = y - 2$ **(d)** $2 = 3x - y$

    (e) $3y = 2x - 6$ **(f)** $2y - 6x + 4 = 0$

Exercise 18vi

Links: 18F

> ### What you should know
>
> Equations for straight lines can always be written in the form $y = mx + c$, where m is the gradient and c is the y-intercept.

1 Write the following equations in the form $y = mx + c$. For each line, state the gradient and y-intercept values.

    (a) $2y = 4x + 12$ **(b)** $5y = 25x - 10$

    (c) $4y = 4x - 8$ **(d)** $6y = 18x + 36$

    (e) $7y = 21x$ **(f)** $8y = 16 - 32x$

    (g) $3y + 12x = 9$ **(h)** $5x - 5y = 35$

    (i) $8 - 2y = 14x$ **(j)** $8y = 0$

    (k) $12x + 6y = -18$ **(l)** $y - x - 1 = 0$

> The equation must always begin with "$y = ...$" to obtain the correct values of m and c.

2 Rearrange the following linear equations in the form $y = mx + c$. Express both m and c as fractions.

    (a) $2y = 5x - 7$ **(b)** $3y = 4x + 8$

    (c) $5y = 7x - 8$ **(d)** $10y = -4x - 5$

    (e) $6y + 4x = 3$ **(f)** $3y - 2x = -1$

    (g) $4x + 5y = -3$ **(h)** $x + 6y - 3 = 0$

    (i) $6 - 8x = 10y$

Exercise 18vii

Links: 18G

> ## What you should know
>
> Graphs that contain x^2 in their equations are called quadratic graphs and are curved. The equations are called quadratic equations.

For each of the following graphs:

(a) Make a table of values in the range given.

(b) Plot the points, using sensible y-values, and draw the graph.
Join the points with a smooth curve.

1 $y = x^2$, for x values $-3, -2, -1, 0, 1, 2, 3$

2 $y = x^2 + 3$, for x values $-3, -2, -1, 0, 1, 2, 3$

3 $y = 2x^2 + 3$, for x values $-3, -2, -1, 0, 1, 2, 3$

4 $y = 4x^2 - 3$, for x values $-3, -2, -1, 0, 1, 2, 3$

5 $y = x^2 - x$, for x values $-2, -1, 0, 1, 2, 3$

6 $y = x^2 + 5x$, for x values $-6, -4, -2, 0, 2, 3$

7 $y = 2x^2 - 3x$, for x values $-3, -2, -1, 0, 1, 2, 3, 4$

8 $y = 3x^2 + 2x$, for x values $-4, -3, -2, -1, 0, 1, 2, 3$

Exercise 18viii

Links: 18H

> ## What you should know
>
> All curves of quadratic equations are symmetrical about a line that is parallel to the y-axis.

1 For each graph in questions 1–8 in Exercise 18vii, state the line of symmetry in the form "$x = ...$".

2 For each of the quadratic equations
  (i) make a table of values in the given range
 (ii) draw the graph
(iii) state the equation of the line of symmetry.
  (a) $y = x^2 + x + 1$, for x values $-4, -3, -2, -1, 0, 1, 2, 3$
  (b) $y = 2x^2 - 2x + 3$, for x values $-2, -1, 0, 1, 2, 3$
  (c) $y = x^2 - 5x + 4$, for x values $-2, -1, 0, 1, 3, 5, 7$
  (d) $y = 3x^2 + 2x - 5$, for x values $-3, -2, -1, 0, 1, 2$
  (e) $y = 2x^2 + 4x - 3$, for x values $-3, -1, 0, 1, 2$
  (f) $y = \frac{1}{2}x^2 + 3x - 2$, for x values $-10, -8, -6, -4, -2, 0, 2, 4$

Exercise 18ix

Links: 18I

> ### What you should know
>
> Graphs can be used to solve linear equations by looking at the point of intersection of two straight lines.

1 Draw the graph of $y = x + 7$. It intersects the line $y = 4$ at the point P. What are the coordinates of P?

2 The line $y = 7$ intersects another line $y = 3x - 2$ at a point Q. Draw these graphs and find the coordinates of Q. Where does the line $y = 3x - 2$ cross the x-axis?

3 In each set of equations

   (a) $y = 3x - 2,\ y = 2x + 1$ (b) $y = 4 + 5x,\ y = 3x + 2$

   (i)   draw the lines on the same coordinate grid.
   (ii) write down the coordinates of the point of intersection.

Exercise 18x

Links: 18J

> ### What you should know
>
> Quadratic equations can also be solved graphically by looking at the points of intersection of the curve and a straight line.

1 Draw the curve $y = x^2 + 2$ for values of x between -3 and 3.

   (a) Where does the curve cross the x-axis?

   Now draw the line $y = 3$.

   (b) What are the coordinates of the points of intersection?

   (c) Write down the equation you have just solved.

2 Draw the curve $y = 2x^2 - x$ in the range $x = -2$ to $x = 3$. Now draw the line $y = 6$. Solve the equation $2x^2 - x = 6$ by noting the two points of intersection.

3 (a) Draw the graph of $y = x^2 - 3x + 3$ by creating a table of values for values of x between -2 and 5.

   (b) Solve the equation $x^2 - 3x + 3 = 7$.

4 For each graph drawn in question 2 of Exercise 18viii listed below, solve the quadratic equation written next to the graph.

(a) $y = x^2 + x + 1$; $x^2 + x + 1 = 3$

(b) $y = 2x^2 - 2x + 3$; $2x^2 - 2x + 3 = 7$

(c) $y = x^2 - 5x + 4$; $x^2 - 5x + 4 = 4$

(d) $y = 3x^2 + 2x - 5$; $3x^2 + 2x - 8 = 0$

(e) $y = 2x^2 + 4x - 3$; $2x^2 + 4x - 16 = 0$

(f) $y = \frac{1}{2}x^2 + 3x - 2$; $\frac{1}{2}x^2 + 3x + 4 = 0$

Exercise 18xi

Links: 18K

What you should know

Conversion graphs are used to convert one type of measurement into another, usually with different units.

1 Copy and complete this conversion table between kilograms and grams.

g (x)	0	500		1500	2000	3000	5000
kg (y)	0		1		2		

(a) Draw a conversion graph with x-values between 0 g and 8000 g, and y-values between 0 kg and 8 kg.

From the graph, find

(b) how many kilograms are equivalent to 4200 g

(c) how many grams are equivalent to 7.6 kg

2 Copy and complete the table that converts litres to pints.

Litres (x)	1	2		4	5			8		10
Pints (y)		3.5				10.5		14		17.5

(a) Draw a conversion graph for this data.

(b) One gallon is the same as eight pints. How many litres is this equivalent to?

3 This table shows the conversion between cm^2 and m^2.

m^2 (x)	1	2	3	4	5
cm^2 (y)	10 000	40 000			250 000

(a) Complete the table and draw the area-conversion graph.

(b) What do you notice about this particular graph?

(c) What is this shape called?

(d) What is 3.7 m^2 approximately equivalent to in cm^2?

> Remember that
> 1 m = 100 cm and
> $1 m^2 = 100 \times 100\ cm^2$
>   = 10 000 cm^2

Exercise 18xii

Links: 18L

> ## What you should know
>
> A distance–time graph shows information about a journey. The gradient of any part of the graph gives the speed.
>
> $$\text{speed} = \frac{\text{distance}}{\text{time}}, \quad \text{average speed} = \frac{\text{total distance}}{\text{total time}}$$

1 The distance–time graph below shows a journey from home to the local shops and back.

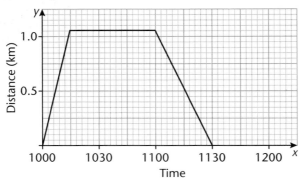

    (a) How long was spent at the shops?

    (b) What was the speed to the shops?

    (c) How long was the shopping trip?

2 The mobile library bus makes its usual journey to the local villages, as shown in the distance–time graph.

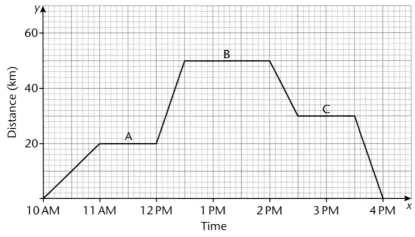

    (a) How many villages were visited that day?

    (b) How long did the bus stop in village B?

    (c) What time did the bus leave to return to the depot?

    (d) What was the speed of the bus on its return journey?

3 Ben walks 3 km home after school every day after the bell, which rings at 3.40 PM. He always visits the local sweet shop 1.25 km from school, which takes him 15 mins. He spends 10 mins inside the shop before continuing his journey and arriving home at 4.25 PM. Draw a distance−time graph for Ben's journey and work out:

Remember, time is usually given along the x-axis, distance up the y-axis.

(a) his speed from school to the shop

(b) his speed from the shop to home

(c) his average speed for the whole journey.

Give your answers in km/h.

Mixed Exercise

1 Two points, A and B, have coordinates $(10, -4)$ and $(-2, -6)$. Work out the coordinates of the mid-point of line AB.

2 What is the equation of a straight line that goes through the points $(0, 0)$ and $(2, 2)$?

3 For the following straight lines, give the values of the gradient (m) and intercept (c).

(a) $y = 5x + 3$ **(b)** $y = -2x - 8$

(c) $2y = 6x - 10$ **(d)** $y - x + 1 = 0$

(e) $2x + 3y = 12$

4 (a) Plot the graph of $y = 3x - 5$ by making a table, using x values $-1, 0$ and 1.

(b) Another line, with the equation $y = 6x - 6$, intersects at the point P. Extend the table to include this line. What are the coordinates of the point P?

5 (a) Plot the quadratic equation $y = 3x^2 - 6x + 8$ for values between -1 and 3.

(b) What is the equation of the line of symmetry?

(c) The curve intesects the line $y = 8$ at two points. Use your graph to find the coordinates of these two points.

(d) Write an equation for part **(c)** that gives these solutions.

6 An approximate conversion between °C and °F is given by the following equation:

   °F = $2 \times$ °C + 32

(a) Using this expression, copy and complete the table of values.

°C	10	30	50	70	90	110
°F	52				212	

(b) Draw the conversion graph for this data.

(c) What are the approximate temperatures of ice and boiling water in terms of the Fahrenheit (°F) scale?

7 The distance−time graph shows John's train journey to work each morning.

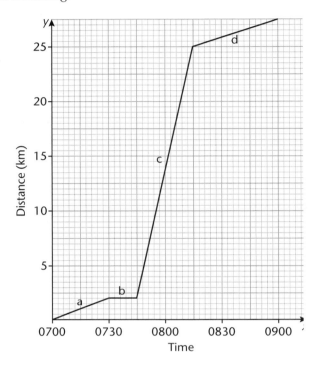

(a) How long does John wait for the train?

(b) What is the speed of the train journey?

(c) How long does it take him to get to work?

Checklist

You should know how to...	Grade	For more help, look back at Student Book pages...
write coordinates in all four quadrants	G/F	458–459
plot and draw straight-line graphs	E/D	463–474
plot and draw quadratic curves	C	474–480
work out coordinates of points of intersection when two graphs cross	C	480–487
plot conversion graphs	F/E	487–489
interpret and use distance−time graphs.	E to C	490–494

Exercise 19i

Links: 19A

> **What you should know**
>
> When you reflect a shape in a mirror line, the object and image are congruent.
> Every point on an object reflects to an image point on the opposite side of the mirror line.
> To describe a reflection fully, you need to give the equation of the mirror line.

1 Each diagram shows an object with its image. Copy the diagrams onto squared paper and draw in the mirror line in each case.

(a)

(b)

> You will need squared paper for each question in this exercise.

(c)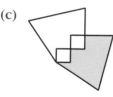

(d)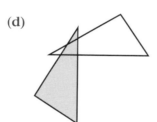

2 Copy these shapes and the dashed mirror line onto squared paper. Draw the reflected image in each case.

(a)

(b)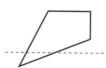

(c)

(d)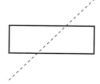

3 Copy the axes and the shape *ABCD* onto squared paper.

(a) Reflect the shape along the *x*-axis and label the image *A′B′C′D′*.

(b) What is the equation of this mirror line?

(c) Now reflect *ABCD* along the line *x* = −1 and label this image *A″B″C″D″*.

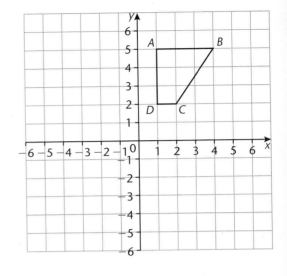

4 Copy the axes and the shape *EFG* onto squared paper.

Reflect this shape in the mirror line given by the equation *x* = 1 and label this image *E′F′G′*. Now reflect this new shape in the mirror line *y* = *x* and label this new image *E″F″G″*.

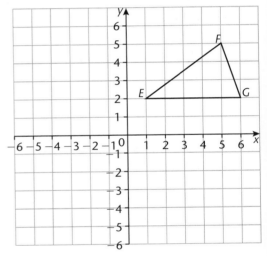

Exercise 19ii

Links: 19B

What you should know

A rotation turns an object either clockwise or anticlockwise through a given angle about a centre of rotation. This can be either inside or outside the object. To describe a rotation you need to specify the direction of rotation, the angle of rotation and centre of rotation.

1 Copy these shapes onto squared paper. Rotate each shape about the point *P*:

(i) a quarter-turn clockwise

(ii) a half-turn anticlockwise.

(a)

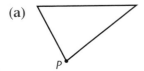

(b)

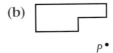

(c) 　　　**(d)**

2 Copy this shape onto squared paper and draw the image after it has been rotated about the point *P*.

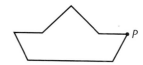

  (a) 180° clockwise

  (b) 270° anticlockwise

  (c) a quarter-turn anticlockwise.

3 On squared paper, draw *x*- and *y*-axes from −6 to 6. Copy the shape *G* onto your axes.

  Draw the image after it has been rotated

  (a) through 90° clockwise about the origin (0, 0). Label this image *G′*.

  (b) a half-turn anticlockwise about the point (0, 1). Label this image *G″*.

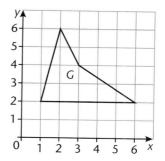

4 Describe fully the transformation that maps the shape H onto the shape I.

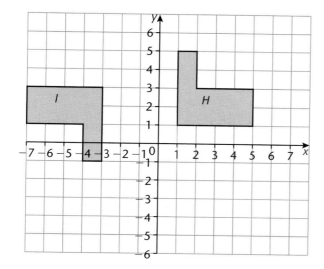

Exercise 19iii

Links: 19C

> **What you should know**
>
> A translation slides a shape from one point to another. To describe a translation, you need to give the distance and the direction of the movement. You can describe a translation by a column vector $\left(\frac{a}{b}\right)$.

1 Copy these shapes onto squared paper and translate each one of them by the amounts shown.

    (a) $\begin{pmatrix} 2 \\ 3 \end{pmatrix}$ **(b)** $\begin{pmatrix} -2 \\ 1 \end{pmatrix}$ **(c)** $\begin{pmatrix} -4 \\ -3 \end{pmatrix}$

2 Copy this shape onto squared paper.

A translation of the shape moves the point X to the point X' on the image.

    (a) Draw the complete image.

    (b) What is the column vector that describes the translation?

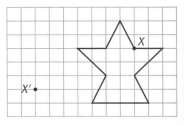

3 The shape P is translated to new positions Q, R, S, T and U.

Describe each translation by giving the column vector.

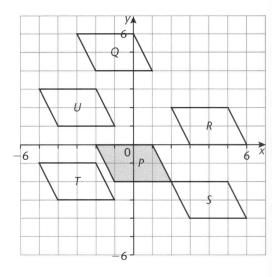

Exercise 19iv

Links: 19D, 19E

What you should know

An enlargement changes the size of an object but not its shape (i.e. the object and image are similar). The number of times a shape is enlarged is called the *scale factor*. It is a positive whole number or a fraction. The position of an enlargement is determined by the point of the centre of enlargement.

To describe an enlargement, you need to specify the scale factor and centre of enlargement.

1 For each of the following shapes, work out the scale factor of the enlargement. The object shape is shown shaded.

(a)   (b)   (c)

2 Copy each of the following shapes onto squared paper. Enlarge each shape by the scale factor shown in brackets.

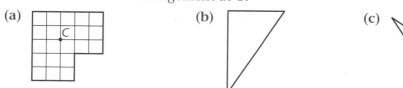

(a)   (b)   (c)   (d)

(4)   (3)   (2)   (2)

3 Copy the following shapes onto squared paper. Enlarge each one by a scale factor of 2 from the centre of enlargement at *C*.

(a)   (b)   (c)

4 The object *Y* is enlarged to produce the image *X*. Copy the shapes onto squared paper.

(a) What is the scale factor of the enlargement?

(b) Construct lines to show the position of the centre of enlargement.

(c) What are the co-ordinates of the centre of enlargement?

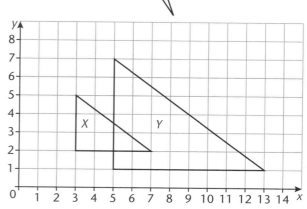

Exercise 19v

> **What you should know**
>
> Congruent shapes are exactly the same shape and exactly the same size. Similar shapes have exactly the same shape but are not the same size.
>
> The four rules for proving that two triangles are congruent: side, side, side (SSS); side, angle, side (SAS); angle, side, angle (ASA) or angle, angle, side (AAS); and right angle, hypotenuse, side (RHS).

1 Look at the shapes in the diagram. Compared with the shaded shape in the diagram, which shapes are

(a) similar (b) congruent (c) neither?

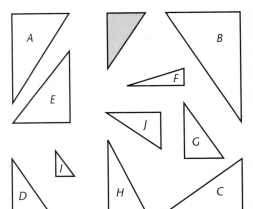

2 Copy these shapes onto squared paper. For each shape, draw an image that is

(i) congruent (ii) similar.

What are the scale factors for the similar shapes that have been drawn?

(a) (b) (c)

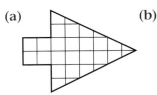

3 For each pair of triangles, identify which ones are congruent and give the appropriate reasons.

(a)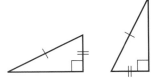

(b)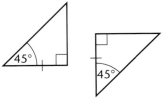

(c)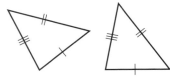

(d)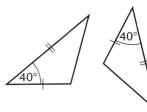

4 Look at the following pairs of triangles. For each pair, identify whether they
are congruent or not. Give an appropriate reason for thier congruency.

(a)

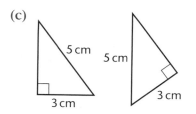

(b)

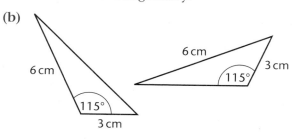

(c)

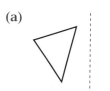

(d)

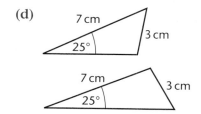

Mixed Exercise

1 Copy these shapes on to squared paper and reflect each shape in the
mirror line shown.

(a)

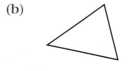

(b)

(c)

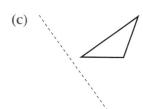

2 Copy the diagram and rotate the shape *T* through 90° anticlockwise about the point *P*. Label this *T'*.

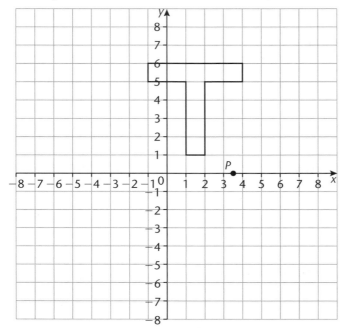

Now reflect this new shape in the mirror line *x* = 1 and label this new shape *T"*.

3 Copy the shape *Q* onto squared paper, translate it through the vector $\begin{pmatrix} -6 \\ -4 \end{pmatrix}$ and label this new shape *Q'*.

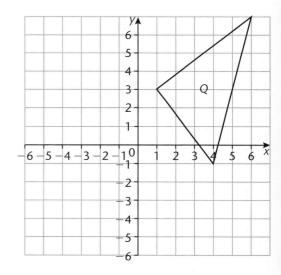

4 Copy the following shape onto squared paper and enlarge it by a scale factor of 2 about the point *P*.

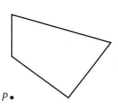

5 Look at the following triangles.

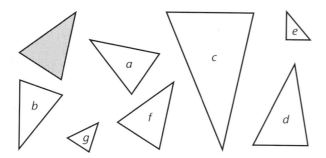

Compared with the shaded shape, which triangles are

(a) similar

(b) congruent

(c) neither?

6 Are the following triangles congruent? If so, give the appropriate reasons.

(a)

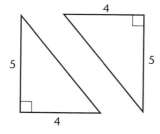

(b)

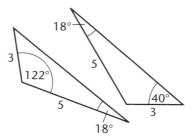

Checklist

You should know how to...	Grade	For more help, look back at Student Book pages...
recognise and use the four types of transformation: reflection, rotation, translation and enlargement	G to C	498–516
find the centre and scale factor of an enlargement	C	510–516
identify congruent and similar shapes	G	517–520
use the congruence properties to identify congruent triangles.	C	518–521

20 Averages

Exercise 20i

Links: 20A

What you should know

The mean is the sum of all the data values divided by the number of values.
The mode is the value that occurs most often.
The median is the middle value when the data is arranged in order of size.
The range is the difference between the highest and lowest values.

1 Find the mean, mode, median and range for these data sets.
   (a) 3, 9, 7, 8, 1, 1, 7, 6, 5, 5, 3, 1, 4, 2
   (b) 100, 101, 105, 99, 97, 104, 101, 100, 98
   (c) 27, 36, 41, 29, 32, 28, 40, 37, 35, 30, 39, 41
   (d) 523, 516, 576, 542, 533, 527, 588, 544, 516, 528

2 Find the mean, mode, median and range for these data sets.
   (a) 16.8, 17.1, 16.5, 17.4, 16.6, 18.1, 17.7, 16.9, 17.3
   (b) 0.6, 0.7, 0.5, 0.5, 0.6, 0.8, 1.1, 0.4, 0.7, 0.4, 0.5
   (c) 122.1, 120.3, 140.7, 133.8, 139.7, 136.4, 138.9, 127.6, 131.2, 125.2, 134.4, 129.3
   (d) 5.62, 5.74, 5.83, 5.76, 5.68, 5.81, 5.73, 5.79, 5.62, 5.74

Exercise 20ii

Links: 20B

What you should know

Σx means the sum of all the x values $= x_1 + x_2 + \ldots + x_n$.
The mean $\bar{x}$ is given by $\frac{\Sigma x}{n}$.

In each of the questions below, begin by finding the value of Σx to help you work out the mean value, $\bar{x}$.

1 In a hockey tournament, the number of goals scored in each match were recorded as follows.

   2, 1, 0, 0, 3, 5, 0, 1, 2, 4, 0, 1, 2, 3, 2, 2

   Find the mean, mode, median and range for the number of goals scored.

2 The mass of ten apples were recorded.

   100 g, 104 g, 112 g, 92 g, 96 g, 97 g, 105 g, 110 g, 105 g, 90 g

   Find the mean, mode, median and range of the mass of the apples.

3 The mass (in tonnes) of eight lorries entering a waste disposal site were measured.

22.6, 28.1, 20.5, 23.4, 24.7, 19.8, 21.8, 25.1

Find the mean, mode, median and range of the mass of the lorries.

4 The speeds of cars on a local road were measured with a speed gun, and the following results were recorded in a stem-and-leaf diagram.

```
2 | 7 7 8 9
3 | 0 0 1 1 2 2 2 3 3 3 3 4 4 4 5 7 7 8 8 9
4 | 0 1 4 7 7 8
5 | 2 6
```

The key 3|4 means 34 mph.

(a) Find the mean, mode, median and range of the speeds on this road.

(b) What is the probable speed limit for this road?

Exercise 20iii

Links: 20C

What you should know

Sometimes the best average is not always the mean. A better average might be obtained by leaving out the extreme values.

1 In a snooker tournament, the highest breaks recorded by one particular player were as follows:

36, 27, 68, 51, 120, 46, 9, 40, 22, 37, 19

(a) What is the mean break score?

(b) Is this a sensible average to use for this player?

2 In a 400 m school running event, the following times were recorded (in seconds) by the athletes.

76, 68, 82, 60, 72, 69, 65, 75, 76, 81, 117, 63

(a) Find the mean, mode and median times for this event.

(b) What would be the more sensible average to use?

(c) What would be the mean value if the extreme time of 117 s was omitted?

Exercise 20iv

Links: 20D

What you should know

The frequency (f) is the number of times an answer or result occurs in the data.

For a large amount of data (x), you can tally your results into a frequency table.

For grouped data, the mean is given by $\bar{x} = \dfrac{\Sigma fx}{\Sigma x}$.

1   The number of mobile phone calls made each day were recorded
over a four-week period.

5, 6, 7, 7, 6, 11, 10, 6, 5, 6, 8, 9, 9, 12

8, 9, 5, 7, 5, 8, 11, 9, 5, 11, 6, 6, 12, 5

(a) Copy and complete the frequency table below.

Number of calls (x)	Tally	Frequency (f)	fx
5	ⅢⅠ	6	30
6			
7			
8			
9			
10	Ⅰ	1	10
11			
12			
		$\Sigma f =$	$\Sigma fx =$

(b) Find the mean, mode, median and range for this data.

2   In Morse code, letters of the alphabet and the numbers $0-9$ are represented
by a series of dots and dashes. The number of dots and dashes used can be
seen in the following table.

Dots (x)	Frequency (f)	fx	Dashes (x)	Frequency (f)	fx
0	4		0	5	
1	11		1	12	
2	10		2	10	
3	7		3	6	
4	3		4	2	
5	1		5	1	

(a) Copy and complete the table to include the fx values.

(b) Find the mean, mode and median for both dots and dashes.

3 A local hockey team secretary kept a record of the number of goals scored during the season 2004−2005, as shown in the table.

Number of goals (x)	0	1	2	3	4	5
Frequency (f)	6	4	7	1	2	1

(a) Copy and extend the table to include the values of fx.

(b) Work out the values of Σf and Σfx.

(c) From these values, calculate the mean number of goals scored.

Exercise 20v   Links: 20E

> ### What you should know
>
> Large data sets are best grouped together into class intervals. The end points of class intervals are called class limits and the mid-interval value is the mean of the two class limits.
>
> The class interval containing the median is called the median class interval.
>
> The class interval with the highest frequency is called the modal class interval.
>
> Only an estimated mean can be obtained from a grouped frequency table.

1 An RAC support vehicle records the number of incidents they attend during a two-week period.

Number of visits	Frequency (f)	Mid-interval value (x)	fx
3−4	7	3.5	
5−6	20		
7−8	36		
9−10	5	9.5	
11−12	2		23
	$\Sigma f =$		$\Sigma fx =$

(a) Copy and complete the table. Use the information to estimate the mean number of visits.

(b) What are the modal and median class intervals?

2 The heights of 32 members of the sixth form selected at random were recorded in a table.

Height, h (cm)	Frequency (f)	Mid-interval value (x)	fx
$140 \leqslant h < 150$	2		
$150 \leqslant h < 160$	3		
$160 \leqslant h < 170$	6		
$170 \leqslant h < 180$	9		
$180 \leqslant h < 190$	9		
$190 \leqslant h < 200$	2		
$200 \leqslant h < 210$	1		
	$\Sigma f =$		$\Sigma fx =$

(a) Copy and complete the grouped frequency table. Use the table to estimate the mean height of the group.

(b) What are the modal and median height class intervals?

3 In the design-and-technology storeroom, the lengths of wood were measured and the results recorded in the following table.

Length, l (cm)	Frequency (f)
$20 \leqslant l < 30$	13
$30 \leqslant l < 40$	12
$40 \leqslant l < 50$	19
$50 \leqslant l < 60$	10
$60 \leqslant l < 70$	2

(a) Extend the table to include the mid-interval values for the length (call this x) and the values of fx. Include the values of Σf and Σfx.

(b) Estimate the mean length of the wood in the store.

(c) What are the modal and median class intervals for the length of wood in the store?

Mixed Exercise

1 Find the mean, mode, median and range for these data sets.

(a) 36, 10, 24, 0, 56, 20, 6, 12, 10, 18

(b) 7.2, 6.7, 8.3, 7.7, 8.1, 8.0, 5.9, 6.2, 7.7

(c) 0.05, 0.03, 0.07, 0.06, 0.06, 0.07, 0.08, 0.05, 0.06

2 The population of the various districts in Cheshire in mid-2003 were as follows.

Give your answers correct to 4 s.f.

119 100, 91 500, 112 700, 81 000, 150 300, 124 100

Work out the mean, median and range for this data.

3 The salaries of the work force in a small company were as follows.

£20 500, £18 700, £15 200, £16 300, £22 800, £39 950, £19 800, £18 700

(a) Find the mean, mode, median and range of the salaries.

(b) What is the most sensible *average* that best describes the salaries?

Give your answers correct to 4 s.f.

(c) What is the mean value when the Director's salary of £39 950 is not included?

4 The list shows the number of goals scored by a school football team in their last 22 matches.

2, 0, 1, 5, 0, 3, 0, 7, 2, 4, 3, 0, 2, 2, 0, 1, 4, 6, 2, 0, 1, 3

(a) Construct a frequency table for this set of data.

(b) From the table, work out Σf and Σfx.

(c) Calculate the mean, mode and median number of goals scored.

5 In an experiment, the voltage of used AA batteries was recorded. The results are shown below.

Voltage (volts)	Frequency (*f*)
$0.0 < v \leqslant 0.3$	2
$0.3 < v \leqslant 0.6$	7
$0.6 < v \leqslant 0.9$	5
$0.9 < v \leqslant 1.2$	13
$1.2 < v \leqslant 1.5$	9

(a) Copy and extend the table to include the mid-interval values (call this *x*).

(b) Work out the values of Σf and Σfx.

(c) Estimate the mean voltage of the used batteries.

(d) What is the voltage value for a new AA battery?

Checklist

You should know how to...	Grade	For more help, look back at Student Book pages...
find the average (mean, median and mode) and the range for discrete data	G to C	527–532
decide which is the best average to use	E to C	532–538
find the mean, median and mode from frequency distributions of both discrete and continuous data.	E to C	538–543

Exercise 21i

Links: 21A, 21B

> ### What you should know
>
> In any right-angled triangle (one with a 90° angle) with sides a, b and c, the square of the longest side – the hypotenuse (c) – is equal to the sum (adding) of the squares on the other two sides.
>
> $$c^2 = a^2 + b^2$$
>
>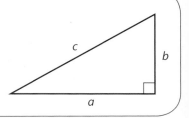

In this exercise give your answers to 1 decimal place when appropriate.

1   Use Pythagoras' Theorem to calculate the length of the longest side in each of these triangles

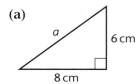

2   Calculate the lengths marked with letters.

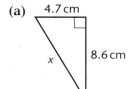   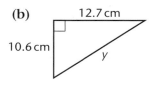   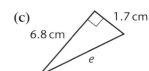   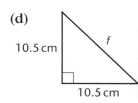

3   A door is 2.3 m high and 0.9 m wide. Calculate the length of the door diagonal.

4   A flagpole stands 3.7 m high and is kept vertical by a series of taut guy ropes 5 m away from the pole. What is the length of each of the guy ropes?

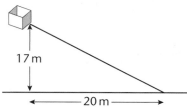

5   A box kite is flying at a height of 17 m above level ground in a strong wind. The string is taut and the child holding the string is 20 m away from the kite. How long is the string?

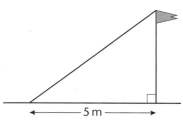

6 An aeroplane flying at 3000 m is on approach to a runway 10 km away. How far does the aeroplane have to fly before touching down on the runway?

7 An A-frame tent is being erected. If the centre pole is 2.1 m tall and the base of the tent is 3.6 m wide what is the length of the tent side?

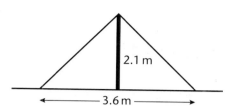

8 Two points P and Q have coordinates P(6, 3) and Q(12, 7). Find the length of the line PQ.

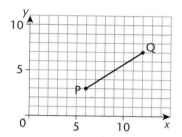

Exercise 21ii

Links: 21C

What you should know

To find the lengths of the shorter sides use the following formulae.

$$a^2 = c^2 - b^2 \qquad b^2 = c^2 - a^2$$

In this exercise give your answers to 1 decimal place where appropriate.

1 Calculate the lengths marked with letters in the following triangles:

(a)
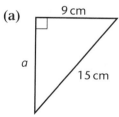

(b)
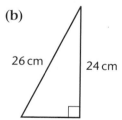

(c)
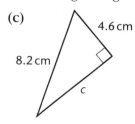

(d)
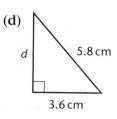

2 Calculate the lengths marked with letters.

(a)
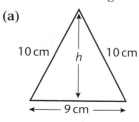

(b)
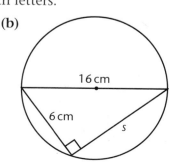

3 A garden shed has the dimensions shown on the right. Find the height of the shed above the level ground.

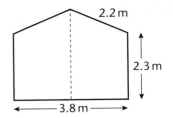

4 A ladder 3.5 m long leans against a vertical wall. If the foot of the ladder is 1.8 m from the wall how far does the ladder reach up the wall?

5 A square has a diagnonal length of 12 cm. What is the side length of the square?

6 A cone has a base radius of 5 inches and a slant height of 10 inches. What is the vertical height of the cone?

Mixed Exercise

1 A small fishing boat leaves port and sails 6 km due south before turning due west and travelling a further 7.5 km. How far is the fishing boat from the port?

2 A flatscreen colour monitor is 14.1 inches wide and 12.8 inches high. What is the length of the screen diagonal? (Give your answer to the nearest inch).

3 A rocket travelled a straight-line distance of 80 km from its launch pad 25 km away. What is the maximum height the rocket reached? (Give your answer to the nearest km).

4 A triangle is drawn inside a semicircle so that the right angle just touches the circle, as shown in the figure. If the diameter of the circle is 10 cm what are the lengths of the sides of the triangle?

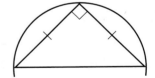

Checklist

You should know how to...	Grade	For more help, look back at Student Book pages...
understand Pythagoras' Theorem	C	546–547
calculate the longest side (the hypotenuse) of a right-angled triangle	C	548–549
calculate one of the shorter sides of a right-angled triangle	C	550–551
apply Pythagoras' Theorem to solving 'real' problems.	C	550–553

22 Proof

Exercise 22i

Links: 22A

> **What you should know**
>
> Verify means to check something is true by substituting numbers into an expression or formula. It is a practical demonstration.
> Proof means to show something is true using logical reasoning.

1 p is an odd number and q is an even number.

    (a) Explain why $p - q + 1$ is always an even number.

    (b) Explain why $p(q + 1)$ is always an odd number.

2 n is a positive integer greater than 1.
    Explain why $n^2 - n$ must always be an even number.

3 x is an even number.
    Explain why $x^2 + 3$ is always an odd number.

4 If p is an odd number, prove that $(p + 2)(p - 2)$ is an odd number.

5 m is an odd number and n is an even number.

    (a) Explain why mn is always an even number.

    (b) Explain why $(m + n)(2n + 1)$ is always an odd number.

Exercise 22ii

Links: 22B

> **What you should know**
>
> To prove by counter example, find one example where the stated result does not work.

1 m is an even number.
    Steve says that $m^2 - \frac{1}{2}m$ will never end in a zero.
    Give an example to show that Steve is wrong.

2 a and b are consecutive prime numbers where $a < b$.
    Simon says that $2a + b$ always gives a prime number.
    Give an example to show that he is wrong.

3 p is a whole number.
    Kim says that $2p^2 + 5$ is never a multiple of 5.
    Give an example to show that she is wrong.

4 Jo says that $n^2 + 10n + 1$ is not prime for any integer value of n.
Give a counter example to show that she is wrong.

5 x and y are consecutive prime numbers.
Jon says that the answer to $x \times y$ can never end in a 9.
Give a counter example to show that he is wrong.

Mixed exercise

1 p, q and r are consecutive integers.

  (a) Explain why $pr + q$ is always an odd number.

  (b) Will $p \times q \times r$ be odd, even or can it be either?
  Explain your answer.

2 p is an odd number and q is an even number.
Is the expression $pq + (p + q)^2 + 4$ odd, even or can it be either?

3 Grace says that $2n^2 + 17n + 8$ is never a square number for
any integer value of n.
Give a counter example to show that she is wrong.

Checklist

You should know how to...	Grade	For more help, look back at Student Book pages...
verify that a statement is true	E	555–558
prove that a statement is true	D/C	555–558
use proof by counter example to show a statement is not true	D/C	558–559
prove geometrical results.	C	560–561